To Mary
On our Second Wedding Anniversary.

from Roger

Seashells of Oman

Seashells of Oman

By Donald and Eloise Bosch
Edited by Kathleen Smythe

Longman Group Limited
London and New York

Longman Group Limited
Longman House Burnt Mill
Harlow Essex England

© Longman Group Limited 1982
*All rights reserved. No part of this publication
may be reproduced, stored in a retrieval system
or transmitted in any form or by any means, electronic,
mechanical, photocopying, recording or otherwise,
without the prior permission of the Copyright owner.*

First published 1982

ISBN 0 582 78309 7

British Library Cataloguing in Publication Data

Bosch, Donald
 Seashells of Oman
 1. Shell – Oman – Identification
 I. Title   II. Bosch, Eloise
 594′.0471′095353   QL426.04

 ISBN 0-582-78309.7

Library of Congress Cataloging in Publication Data

Bosch, Donald
 Seashells of Oman.

 Bibliography: p.
 Includes index.
 1. Shells—Oman—Identification. I. Bosch,
 Eloise,   II. Smythe, Kathleen.   III. Title.
 QL426.05B67   594′.0471′095353   81-14236
 ISBN 0-582-78309-7   AACR2

Designed by Roland Blunk MSIAD
Diagrams by Karen Douglas

Set in Monotype Baskerville
by Keyspools Limited, Golborne, Lancashire
Printed and bound in Great Britain by
Collins, Glasgow

To our three children, David, Paul and Bonnie, who have brought much joy to our lives.

Acknowledgements

A book of this nature reflects the contribution and effort of a great many people. Accordingly, the authors wish to recognize and thank those persons who gave so generously of their time and talents.

We are particularly indebted to the following friends for their help and advice: Mr. William E. Old Jr. of the American Museum of Natural History in New York, who, for nearly twenty-five years has stimulated and encouraged us in our study of molluscs, and was our first teacher. Dr. Henry E. Coomans and Mr. R.G. Moolenbeek of the University of Amsterdam, the Netherlands, who spent many months reviewing our shells and contributing much help, particularly on the bivalves. Dr. Akihiko Matsukuma of Kyushu University, Fukuoka, Japan; Dr. Richard S. Houbrick of the Smithsonian Institute, Washington D.C., and Dr. Richard N. Kilburn of the Natal Museum, South Africa, and Agnes Martis, Personal Assistant, all were most helpful.

Additionally, we are indebted to those who so generously assisted our scientific editor, Mrs. Kathleen Smythe. These friends include Dr. A. Beu, Dr. June E. Chatfield, Mr. M. Dixon, Dr. A. Kohn, Mr. A.P.H. Oliver and Mr. T. Pain. A special thanks is expressed to the staff of the British Museum (Natural History), particularly Mrs. Aileen Blake, Dr. C.P. Nuttall, Dr. J. Taylor, Mrs. Kathie M. Way and Mrs. Solene Whybrow.

Many photographs were taken by Mr. Joe Schad, whose talents are obvious in the pictures. For the hundreds of hours he spent taking pictures, we are indeed appreciative. Thanks are also due to Mr. Trevor Clifford of the Photographic Department of Longman.

We are grateful to those who took the trouble to research and describe the four species which we have discovered. Dr. R. Tucker Abbott of Greenville, Delaware, described Actcon eloiseae *Abbott 1973, and he, in conjunction with Mr. Hal Lewis of Philadelphia, described* Cymatium boschi *Abbott and Lewis 1970. Mr. Phillip W. Clover of Glen Ellen, California, described* Volvarina pergrandis *Clover 1974, and* Conus boschi *Clover 1972.*

For a few of the shells used in some of the photographs we are indebted to our fellow collectors, Kory, Kelly and Kally Jo Wittman, Nel and Hannie de Graaf, Werner and Danielle Fretz, Charlotta Hagstrom, and Noel Pettigrew.

We are grateful to our son, David and his wife, Leslie; our daughter, Bonnie and her husband, Carlos Apcar; and our son, Paul; all of whom made major contributions to our hobby, often using most of their vacation time in search of shells.

Finally, to the many friends who encouraged us to write this book, we owe the ultimate acknowledgement: the motivation to do it.

Contents

The impetus which stimulated the authors to produce this book, was the repeated question raised by friends all over the world, "Why don't you publish something about Oman's seashells? We need a book which specifically covers this area." The challenge was there and many professional friends were ready to help. Our twenty-five years of shell collecting in Oman proved too compelling to ignore.

Our basic objectives were to produce a book which would contain the following:

An artistic presentation of color photographs which would make identification easy but would also leave the viewer with a sense of wonder and appreciation. Few living creatures reflect The Creator's ingenuity and imagination as strikingly as do the molluscs.

A scientific compilation of the seashells of Oman to aid both the scientific investigator and also the amateur collector.

A handbook which would become the particular friend of anyone walking the beaches of Oman or diving in her offshore waters, and who, having found a mollusc, would like to know its proper identification.

No attempt to be exhaustive in the study of molluscs can be successful, and the authors make no claim to present all the living molluscs in Oman. Without doubt, many new species are waiting to be discovered and many known species may ultimately be reclassified. We do hope, however, that the average collector in Oman will discover that most of the shells he finds are described in this book.

Since earliest historical times the Arabian Peninsula has been a major and mystical source of conchological treasures. The first attempts at culturing pearls were made in the Gulf long before the time of Christ or Mohammed. Arabian seashells have been found in Ancient Egyptian tombs, and the Greeks and Romans carried back specimens to Pompeii and other centers of commerce. And the first printed books of Europe, dating from 1551, carried illustrations of Red Sea shells by such early naturalists as Adam Lonicer of Frankfurt and Guillaume Rondelet of Montpellier.

No serious molluscan explorations were undertaken along the shores of Arabia until the Danish zoologist, Peter Forsskål ventured into the Red Sea in the early 1700's. He described a number of new species from the area. However, the major and most spectacular discoveries did not occur until the late 1890's when the British began testing the ocean bottom in preparation for the laying of a transcontinental cable from London to Calcutta.

Captain Frederick W. Townsend, in the course of his cable-laying duties, collected no less than 600 species of shells new to science from the Arabian and Iranian coast. Most of these were described by the English conchologists, J.C. Melvill and Robert Standen between 1893 and 1915. Since those days little collecting has been done, except by amateur shell collectors associated with oil companies.

The authors of this book, Donald and Eloise Bosch, are splendid examples of how enthusiastic collectors of specimen shells can add to our knowledge of malacology. Their respective duties as medical officer and teacher in Oman gave them an opportunity to re-open this rich and little-known shelling area of the world. Tributes to them are in the form of recently described species – Conus boschi, Cymatium boschi *and* Acteon eloiseae. *And now this useful guide to the common shells of Oman gives us an intimate account of these Arabian marine treasures.*

R. Tucker Abbott, President

Regarding taxonomy

Biologists classify living creatures by studying their physical structure (anatomy), how this works (physiology), and how the animal manages to survive (functional morphology). All animals are grouped into Phyla, one such Phylum being the Molluscs.

Some have jokingly said that a mollusc is hard outside, soft inside, and has a slippery skin. Actually a mollusc is a soft-bodied animal which has a fleshy, curtain-like fold of tissue called the mantle, which usually produces an internal or external shell, though a few Genera have no shells at all. In marine molluscs the mantle builds the shell out of calcium carbonate extracted from the sea. Most gastropod molluscs have a ribbon-like set of teeth called the radula with which they can scrape up food or even drill holes in other molluscs. Most molluscs have a foot and all have a simple nervous system. They have variously developed digestive, circulatory and reproductive systems, and many are confined to specialized habitats. It is estimated that there may be as many as 80,000 different species of molluscs. Creatures such as sand dollars, starfish, barnacles and crabs are not molluscs. All molluscs are divided into six Classes as follows:

Gastropoda *stomach-footed*
There are about 30,000 marine species in this Class. These are either one-shelled animals (univalves) such as the most commonly known seashells – conches, cowries, cones, etc. or shell-less ones such as sea-slugs or sea-butterflies. They are either herbivorous or carnivorous. In this class are most land snails. These shells grow in spiral coils around a central pillar. The majority have the apertures on the right when held with the apex upwards.

Bivalvia *two-valved*
There are about 10,000 species in this Class. They have two shelly halves, connected by a hinge ligament, muscles and interlocking teeth. Where the mantle is attached to the two halves of the shell is a line, called the pallial line. This is sometimes indented, and is called the pallial sinus, if the animal has siphons. The pattern of the teeth, muscle scars and pallial line are important identifying features. All bivalves are filter feeders and many are sessile: that is they are attached to one place by threads called a byssus or live in holes excavated from the rock or in timber. Most of the others burrow in the sand. A few species can swim by emitting jets of water from the shells.

Terms used to describe a Gastropod Shell

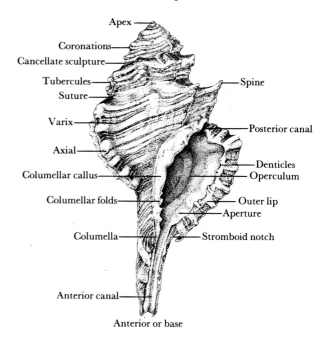

Terms used to describe a Bivalve Shell

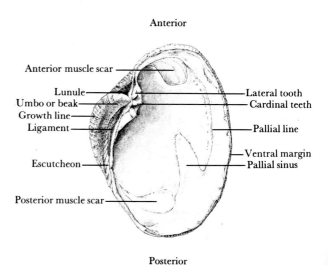

Cephalopoda *head-footed*

There are about 500 species in this Class. These are the squids, octopuses and nautiluses. Anatomical studies of the embryological development, the mantle and the radular teeth have demonstrated that these animals belong to the molluscan phylum.

Scaphopoda *boat-footed*

There are about 1,000 species in this Class. These are the "tusk shells", so called because they resemble a miniature elephant's tusk.

Amphineura *nerves on both sides*

There are about 600 species in this Class. These are the Chitons, all of which usually have 8 oblong shelly plates across the back, although aberrant members with 7 or 9 plates have been found.

Monoplacophora *bearing one plate*

The number of species is unknown. This is a very primitive limpet-like mollusc dredged from deep water. The only known member of this Class, which lives in this area, the extremely fragile *Neopilina adenensis* Tebble, is highly unlikely to be cast up on any beach.

A major problem facing marine biologists is the obvious difficulty in obtaining living specimens from the ocean's depths. And since accurate classification depends upon accurate information, it has often been impossible to decide where certain specimens fit into the taxonomic system. In the particular case of seashells, the durable shell is sometimes the only available thing to study, the soft-bodied animal having long since been destroyed. The vexing questions which have perplexed conchologists exist because all of the facts are not known. As time goes on and more accurate information is obtained, some species may be given different designations, some may be grouped together while others may be separated. But, in the meantime, conchologists, limited frequently by having only the shell to study, are forced to classify all available material as best they can. Some specialists have believed that minor differences in shell structure indicate different species and hence they have given new names to shells which are closely related. These collectors are dubbed "splitters" because they split species into additional species or subspecies. A species, by definition, implies creatures that are able to procreate; that is, they are able to reproduce creatures

like themselves, which in turn are also able to reproduce. There are other collectors who prefer to place certain seashells into the same species despite some differences in structure and color. Such collectors are called "lumpers" because they prefer to lump species together pending the availability of sufficient information for accurate classification.

The inconsistencies which have arisen are indeed perplexing to amateurs because various authors have given different names to the same shell. For example, in the cowry family alone, more than 1,000 names have been given to what are probably not more than 200 species. Scientists who study the anatomy of molluscs will readily concede that the biological validity of certain classifications is sometimes impossible to establish. It seems, therefore, that disagreements regarding the limits of certain families or species are going to be a fact of life for years to come. The authors of this book claim no special insight into the problem. We have utilized the writings of many authors and we have consulted leading specialists for assistance in making identifications. Where more than one name seemed to merit mention, we have included the alternative name.

In an attempt to solve these taxonomic discrepancies, biologists have classified all living creatures into groups, which, in descending order, become more and more specialized.
These groups are as follows:
Kingdom
Phylum
Class
Subclass
Order
Superfamily
Family
Genus
Species
Subspecies

The famous Swedish naturalist, Baron Carl von Linné 1707–1778 designated himself by the latinized form of his name *Linnaeus* when writing the *Systema Naturae* in which he established binomial nomenclature; this practice is followed today and refers to both the plant and the animal kingdoms. He wrote it in Latin and many authors, when using the Latin names which he established use the latin form of his name *Linnaeus*.

Others use the Swedish form *Linné* (with an accent); the common abbreviation used is simply the capital letter 'L'.

Binomial nomenclature means that each species will always have two names: the first name denotes its Genus (plural Genera) and starts with a capital letter; the second name is its specific (Species) name and starts with a small initial letter. Thus, the shell called, *Cypraea nebrites* is a shell in the Genus *Cypraea* which is specifically *nebrites*.

The rules of nomenclature are governed by the International Commission for Zoological Nomenclature. This organization uses what is known as the "rule of priority" when a seashell or any other living creature is given a name. This means that the first author who published a proper description of any particular species has the right to give the permanent name. For example, if Joe Scallop in 1900 named a shell, calling it *Pecten smithi*, publishing a proper description, and Pete Oyster in 1901 published a proper description of the same shell, giving it a different name, the name given by Joe Scallop would be considered valid because his publication appeared a year earlier, i.e. it would still be called *Pecten smithi* Scallop, 1900.

It sometimes happens that the original Genus used in describing a species needs to be changed in the light of improved knowledge. In this case, the original author's name is put into brackets. For instance, if Joe Scallop's Pecten is changed to Chlamys, it would be written *Chlamys smithi* (Scallop, 1900).

Occasionally a shell which obviously belongs to a given species appears to have several consistent variations from the normal. A 'subspecies' name is then utilized for accurate identification. The shell called *Cypraea felina fabula* is a shell which is definitely of the species *felina*, but because of consistent variations in color and pattern, it merits the subspecies name *fabula*.

Terms used to describe a Cowry Shell
Dorsal or Upper view

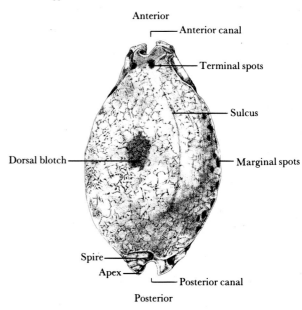

Anterior

Anterior canal

Terminal spots

Sulcus

Dorsal blotch

Marginal spots

Spire

Apex

Posterior canal

Posterior

Ventral view (Ventral or Basal view)

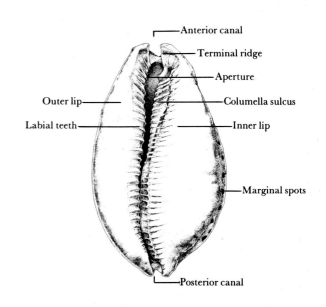

Anterior canal

Terminal ridge

Aperture

Outer lip

Columella sulcus

Labial teeth

Inner lip

Marginal spots

Posterior canal

opposite page
The map shows the Sultanate of Oman with its coastline of over 1000 miles. A glance shows that there are many coves and islands, all of which provide valuable habitat for a wealth of molluscan fauna. Many of the species described in this book come from particular areas: the Musandam Peninsula, the Batinah Coast, Sohar, Barka, As Sib, Muscat, Matrah, Qurayat, Sur, Ras Al Hadd, Masirah, the Khuriya Muriya islands, Hasik, Mirbat, Salalah and Raysut provide the major samplings.

The Sultanate of Oman

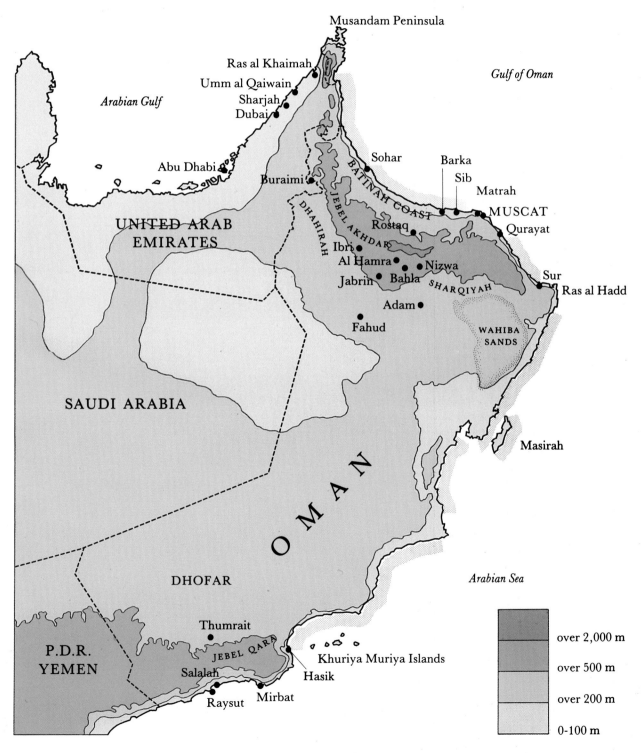

Musandam Peninsula

Gulf of Oman

Ras al Khaimah

Umm al Qaiwain

Arabian Gulf

Sharjah
Dubai

Sohar

Barka

Sib

Matrah

Abu Dhabi

Buraimi

MUSCAT

Qurayat

UNITED ARAB
EMIRATES

BATINAH COAST

JEBEL AKHDAR

DHAHIRAH

Rostaq

Ibri

Al Hamra

Nizwa

Jabrin

Bahla

SHARQIYAH

Sur

Ras al Hadd

Adam

Fahud

WAHIBA
SANDS

SAUDI ARABIA

Masirah

O M A N

Arabian Sea

DHOFAR

Thumrait

JEBEL QARA

P.D.R.
YEMEN

Khuriya Muriya Islands

Salalah

Hasik

Raysut

Mirbat

	over 2,000 m
	over 500 m
	over 200 m
	0-100 m

15

The geological history shaping molluscan life

Geologists consider that a major movement of the
earth's crust began about 12,000,000 years ago in which
the land mass of Arabia broke off from the African
continent, leaving a gap which was filled by water, and
today is represented by the Red Sea. At the same time,
the eastern edge of the Arabian land plate was forced
against the Asian continental plate resulting, at the
zone of compression, in the formation of the Zagros
mountain range in Iran and the Oman mountains
which extend south and south-eastwards from the
Musandam peninsula. The same land movement had a
downward warping effect on the eastern part of the
Arabian plate which eventually sank below sea level
and became the shallow water Gulf which now divides
Iran from the Arabian land mass. The end result of
these massive land movements created the physical
environment along Oman's coasts. At some points, such
as Muscat, the mountains plunge steeply into the sea
leaving no possibility for a sandy shore. At other points,
such as the Batinah coast, wide beaches slope gently
into shallow waters. These various physical patterns
permit the existence of a wide range of molluscan life.
Sand-dwelling molluscs, such as bivalves, olives and
moon shells have hundreds of miles of sandy substrate in
which to live, while at the same time, rock and coral-
dwelling molluscs, such as cowries, nerites, etc., have all
the rock and coral they require to survive. At those
places where rocks and sand meet and mingle, the
molluscan fauna is particularly rich.

Plankton, the basic oceanic food

All ocean dwelling creatures, including molluscs,
ultimately depend upon plankton as their basic food
source. Plankton is a name given to organisms, most of
them microscopic, which drift passively in the water;
some of them are classified as plants, others as animals,
which may be in a larval stage. There are many
thousands of species varying in shape, size, color and
life history. All are inhabitants of the open ocean where
they live suspended in the water. Compared to their
mass they have a relatively large surface area and hence
they float in the ocean at the mercy of the various
currents and surface winds. The plant members of the
plankton community are known as *phytoplankton*
whereas the animal members are called *zooplankton*.
Those organisms living at the air-water interface are
termed *neustons*. Both adult phytoplankton and adult
zooplankton reproduce rapidly thus ensuring the
availability of the basic food source for larger marine
animals. Many molluscs, particularly sessile forms, eat
plankton directly from the water which moves past
them. Other molluscs ingest those creatures which have
eaten the plankton. Thus all molluscs are directly or
indirectly dependent upon plankton for food.
Accordingly, anything which affects the survival of
plankton will secondarily effect the life of seashells. An
oil spill, for example, which suffocates plankton, will
eventually diminish or destroy molluscan life.

Climate of the sea

The survival of a marine mollusc is dependent upon a host of variables in its environment. When optimal surrounding conditions pertain, any given species can be expected to flourish, whereas minimal survival conditions will result in marginal existence or even extinction. It is easily understood that camels cannot live on polar ice, nor can polar bears tolerate the Arabian desert. Each species has definite environmental parameters outside of which it would cease to exist. Molluscs, being living organisms, can continue to live and reproduce only under certain circumstances. But, whereas terrestrial inhabitants face a limited number of variables in their environment, marine molluscs have an astounding range of factors with which to cope. Among these factors are the following: temperature, light, wave action, salinity, ocean currents, biological community interaction and the special problems for inhabitants of the intertidal zone.

Temperature
Ocean currents of varying temperatures constitute one element which influences the water temperature at any particular point; other factors are the surface winds at the air-water interface and the exposure to direct sunlight. The degree of seasonal and daily variation in temperature are maximal in shallow water and minimal in deeper areas. In this region, molluscs living in the intertidal zone face extreme drying heat when the tide is out and then a rapid cooling as the tide moves upwards covering them with water. Such extreme environmental changes create a highly stressed situation, which means that only those creatures capable of withstanding trying conditions are able to survive. Also winter conditions can be very cold in contrast to the high summer temperatures.

Light
Even in clear water sunlight penetrates very little beyond a depth of about 100 meters. Most of the important aspects of photosynthesis occur in shallow water where sunlight, carbon dioxide, water, pigments, certain nutrients and chlorophyll combine to permit green plants to produce organic compounds such as glucose. These organic compounds constitute the energy sources for all inhabitants of the sea. Where adequate sunlight provides the necessary energy fueling for photosynthesis, the living organisms in the area will have plenty of available food. Thus, the climate of this region, providing almost uninterrupted sunlight all

year round, is favorable to the growth and proliferation of all sea life, including molluscs.

Wave action
Few living creatures could withstand the pounding waves which batter certain molluscs. Many of them, such as limpets, cling tenaciously to rocks and are shaped so that waves wash over them easily. Many other molluscs, such as oysters, are permanently attached to one spot and hence are termed "sessile". Still others find protection in rock holes or crevices, thus minimizing the impact of waves.

For those molluscs living on sandy beaches wave action is an extremely important environmental stress factor. Usually they are able to move quickly or dig

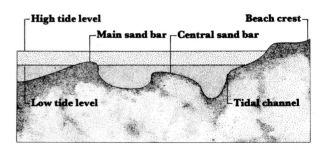

Diagram showing a section through a typical khawr (tidal creek); creeks such as this occur at various places along the coast of Oman. The beach crest descends to a channel which is usually divided by a low central sand bar; the main sand bar at the mouth of the creek is exposed at low tide.

rapidly lest they either be washed into the ocean or else buried too deep in the sand to obtain oxygen and food.

Sessile molluscs find the waves a mixed blessing. On the one hand violent waves threaten to dislodge them, while, on the other hand, the moving water brings them food in the form of plankton and other nutrients. Most sessile molluscs are filter-feeders which means that they obtain their food by filtering sea water through a special apparatus.

Salinity
Ocean water varies in the degree of salt content depending upon temperature, sunlight, evaporation, precipitation and land drainage. The excessively high salt content of the Dead Sea prevents the existence of any life. A few molluscs, such as *Planaxis sulcatus* can

tolerate relative hypersalinity and therefore can be found in high tidal pools where evaporation results in a high salt content in the pool. Fortunately for molluscs living along the coasts of Oman, the salinity of the surrounding ocean is both relatively constant and tolerable, whereas some areas of the neighboring Arabian Gulf have a limited population due to the high salinity.

Ocean currents

Although the ocean may superficially appear to remain quiescent, there is actually a continuous movement of water. As the water column moves about, heavy objects and much dead material gradually sink to the bottom. Important nutrients such as silicates, phosphates and nitrogen compounds sink with dead plankton toward the deeper ocean where they serve as food for the inhabitants of the abyss. In certain areas of the ocean a peculiar water movement occurs which is known as *up-welling*. This phenomenon forces deeper water to circulate toward the surface, bringing with it large quantities of essential nutrients. Thus, where *up-welling* occurs, all forms of sea life are abundant because food is plentiful. This phenomenon of "up-welling" takes place in the Gulf of Oman as well as in the Arabian Sea off the southern coast of Oman, thus providing an almost unvarying temperature throughout the year and constant food supply.

Biological community interaction

All of the various biological species living in any given area, are collectively known as a biological community. These many different species, such as seaweed, fish, molluscs, etc., all are compelled to live in the same environmental situation. They also have to live with each other, or, as sometimes happens, they live by eating each other. Accordingly an inter-relationship exists where the survival of one species can depend entirely upon the availability of another species as a food source. In such instances, the extinction of the preyed-upon species will automatically starve the predator.

Many living creatures both on land and in the sea have special relationships with certain other members of the biological community. When this relationship is one-sided; that is, when one creature benefits at the expense of the other, the recipient is called a parasite. Often however, both parties benefit in a mutually co-operative situation. Many molluscs participate in symbiotic relationships, providing food, housing or protection to other living plants or animals or to each other. The reverse is also true, where non-molluscan life provides special benefits to molluscs. For example, *Cypraea pulchra* makes its home in certain branched corals. Although *Cypraea pulchra* is sometimes found beneath rocks near the coral, it never strays very far from the coral which is its source of food and protection. At times *Cypraea pulchra* becomes "locked" into the branches of the coral where it seems to live happily despite permanent imprisonment.

Special problems for inhabitants of the intertidal zone

Molluscs living in the subtidal zone, that is, at levels always covered by water, have an environment similar to that of fish. Those creatures living in the supratidal zone, that is, above the reach of the tide, have an environment similar to that of terrestrial animals. But those molluscs living in the intertidal zone must contend with extremely stressed situations. Most important is the fact that they are alternately submerged and exposed as the tide ebbs and flows. They must therefore have a respiratory system capable of functioning both above and below water. In many molluscs a specially developed gill apparatus accomplishes this function. Other molluscs enclose sufficient sea water to last them until the tide returns again, by closing the operculum or else by closing their valves tightly together.

Other stress factors which exist in the intertidal zone are the sudden and drastic changes in salinity, temperature, water pressure, sun drying and the availability of food and oxygen. Molluscs able to withstand such difficult circumstances demonstrate those special traits which are essential to survival. Some of them fasten themselves firmly to their substrate; others utilize burrowing skills to get below the surface of the sand; others have thick and heavy shells which serve to insulate them; others are shaped so that wave action has a minimal effect; still others protect themselves by hiding under rocks or in rock crevices. But regardless of the method used, few living creatures can boast the incredible versatility which marks the molluscs' ability to survive under the most adverse circumstances.

Thumbnail answers to common questions

What is the difference between Conchology and Malacology?

The term "Conchology" comes from the Latin *concha* meaning seashell, and hence "Conchology", strictly speaking, implies the study of seashells.

The term "Malacology" comes from the Greek *malakòs* meaning "soft or delicate", and hence "Malacology" implies the study of soft or delicate creatures; that is, the animal which makes the shell.

In point of fact, the two are inseparable. One cannot study molluscs without considering both the soft-bodied animal and its shelly exterior any more than one can study human anatomy without considering both the soft parts and the skeleton. In a sense, a seashell can be thought of as a mollusc's external skeleton. The dichotomy between "Conchology" and "Malacology" should cease to exist since all researchers study the entire animal.

How big and how small do molluscs get?

The largest mollusc is the giant squid, *Architeuthis harveyi*, which can have a body length of twelve feet and has tentacles which can stretch 48 feet, thus giving it a total length of 60 feet. (The base lines of a tennis court are 78 feet apart). This giant squid can weigh up to 600 lbs. The giant clam, *Tridacna gigas* can measure up to four and a half feet and weigh 500 lbs.

The smallest molluscs are virtually microscopic. Some adult clams are no more than one or two mm in length.

Probably at least 80% of all molluscs are less than two inches in adult size. Fewer than five per cent ever exceed three inches.

What is a seashell actually made of?

The main body of a calcareous shell consists of calcium carbonate crystals which are laid down as calcite or aragonite in crossed lamellar layers by the animal's mantle. The various angles of deposition add strength to the shell. The numbers of layers deposited is variable depending upon the species. Small amounts of magnesium carbonate, phosphate and silicate are also present.

External to the main body of the shell is the periostracum, a thin layer consisting mostly of conchiolin, an organic substance related chemically to the chitin found in insects. Some shells, such as the cowries, do not have a periostracum.

The inner layer of the hard shell, lying immediately next to the soft parts, usually consists of calcite which lies parallel to the shell's surface and gives a dull finish. However, some shells have very fine layers of aragonite whose crystals are deposited horizontally, thus creating the mother-of-pearl interior of shells like the abalones. The iridescent mother-of-pearl colors are due to interaction between the crystals and light waves.

How do shells grow? What determines their color and design?

All marine molluscs have a fleshy curtain or cape called the mantle. The special cells on the mantle's margin can extract calcium and other minerals and pigments from the water and deposit these elements on the shell. One can visualize a long, tapering tube, which continually enlarges distally and is coiled upon itself thus producing a spiral staircase effect. The mantle, the architect of the shell, normally builds at the mouth (aperture), thus enlarging the shell. Sometimes, however, the mantle will add to the internal layer thus thickening the shell, or else it may re-absorb previously deposited calcium carbonate so as to increase the space inside the shell.

The production of new shell material is not a constant process but occurs in periodic spurts, depending upon a host of factors which include diet, water temperature and acidity, sexual hormones, and various genetic rhythmical patterns. Growth spurts sometimes leave permanent evidence of previous rest periods in the form of shell sculpturing or ornamentation. Such sculpturing can be in the shape of spines or tubercules, ribs or ridges. In some molluscs, a growth spurt can occur as frequently as every two days, but in most species the spurts probably occur at longer intervals. Adverse conditions can stop growth altogether. As the coiling shell enlarges by additions to the lip, the earliest part of the shell, the spire, gradually becomes out-of-reach of the mantle. Once this happens, that portion of the shell can no longer be repaired, whereas all points of the shell within reach of the mantle can tolerate extensive injury and still be repaired.

The basic colors and designs of seashells are genetically inherited from their parents. Special glands consisting of clumps of color cells are situated along the front margin of the mantle. These shells concentrate the pigments and mix them with fluid calcite before the outer surface hardens. The deposition of pigment can be continuous with shell growth, resulting in a line or band, or it can be intermittent, resulting in dots or dashes. It should be noted that in some molluscs, the most brilliant and variable colors occur in the soft parts rather than in the shell itself. Sometimes the mantle has so extravagantly decorated itself that the shell pales by comparison.

How do molluscs reproduce?

In a group of animals as large and as variable as the molluscs, it is not surprising that many forms of reproduction occur. In many species, such as the limpets, separate sexes exist and the males and females simply spew the sperm and ova into the open ocean where male gamete meets female gamete and fertilization takes place. The enormous odds against the chance meeting of sperm and ova in the open water are compensated for by various environmental and hormonal factors which ensure that both sperm and ova will be excreted simultaneously and in the same general area.

Furthermore, vast numbers, millions, of sperm and ova are discharged into the sea. Only a few of these need to survive in order to procreate the species.

Some molluscs, such as certain clams, are hermaphrodites, that is, both male and female gametes are formed in the same individual so that fertilized eggs are discharged into the sea.

Other molluscs, such as the octopus, have completely separated sexes, and participate in courtship and copulation. The male octopus has even been observed stroking the female in order to arouse her.

Between the extremes of completely heterosexual molluscs and the hermaphroditic ones, are hundreds of different modes of reproduction. There even are some oysters which change their sex periodically, living part of their lives as males and part as females. This is called "rhythmically consecutive sexuality". By their periodic sex change, these humble creatures have obviously found the answer to "the battle of the sexes".

Most molluscs do not take care of their eggs or young, but exceptions do occur; cowries, for example, sit on their eggs like a mother hen.

Upon hatching, many marine molluscs pass through a free-swimming larval stage before becoming a tiny replica of their parents. These veliger larvae usually form part of the plankton.

How old can molluscs become?

There is a paucity of scientific information when age is considered. Some snails are known to reach adulthood and lay fertile eggs in just two weeks from the date of their own birth. Presumably their life expectancy would be equally short. On the other hand, a certain fresh water clam, *Margaritifera margaritifera* has been known to live for 116 years.

On cleaning seashells in Oman

The three basic objectives in the cleaning of living molluscs are:
1. Be as humane as possible to the living creature.
2. Avoid damage to the shell.
3. Get rid of any residual unpleasant odors.

Cleaning methods

Freezing
Immediately upon returning from the beach, put the shells into a dish or pan and place them in the freezing compartment of the refrigerator overnight. A paper towel placed in the bottom of the dish will absorb moisture given off by the shells. The freezing kills the mollusc quickly. The following day the shells can be removed from the refrigerator and allowed to resume room temperature after which the animal can be removed with a bent pin or a dental pick. Optionally, the shells can be taken outside and placed in an open box out of the sun where the ants will commence the cleaning for you. Oman has both large and small ants, all of which consider molluscs a delicacy. After several days with the ants, the shells can be washed out under a stream of water.

Boiling
This method should not be used for shells with a high gloss such as cowries or olives. But it is an excellent method for most other shells. It has added advantages for those who dwell in apartment houses or who have close neighbors, because unpleasant smells are reduced to a minimum. The shells are placed in a stainless steel, aluminium or enamel container, covered with cool water, and put on the stove. Unless the shells are large, a half to one minute of boiling is sufficient. Even large shells do not require more than two minutes of boiling. After boiling, allow the water to return to room temperature following which the animal can be removed with a pin. If there is no time to remove the animals, the shells can be placed outdoors where the ants will commence cleaning almost immediately.

Alcohol
Shells can be soaked in a 70% solution of ethyl alcohol for about three days, after which the animal can usually be removed with a pin.

Burying
Molluscs which have been killed by freezing can be buried in soft sand where bacterial action will rot out the soft parts. Two to four weeks are needed for this process. It can be done indoors if a box of sand is used. Even if buried outdoors it is often wise to bury shells within a box lest individual shells be lost. After a period of rotting the shells can be soaked in water for about an hour and then washed with a stream of water.

Paraffin
Shiny shells such as cowries and olives can easily be cured without damage to the luster by soaking in a closed jar of paraffin, making sure that the opening points downward so that any rotting material which may escape from the shell does not damage the shiny exterior. After two or three days remove the shell (preferably wearing a face mask and well away from other people!) and wash out with a strong jet of water. If necessary the shell can be put in clean paraffin for another day or two.

What not to do
Do not expose shells to prolonged direct sunlight. The sun's rays will destroy the shell's luster and cause fading of the colors. Shells which are placed outside to enlist the help of the ants must be put in the shade or covered in some way.

Do not soak shells in water for more than a few hours. The chemicals released into the water from molluscan tissues will stain the exterior surface of the shells, especially that of the cowries.

Do not boil any shell for more than two minutes. Prolonged boiling causes fine cracks in the enamel. This is particularly true of Oman's beautiful and large *Lambis truncata sebae*. The gorgeous color of the aperture in these shells can be compromised by fine cracking as a result of excessive boiling.

Do not throw away the operculum if there is one. Label it in some way so that you can identify the shell to which it belongs when it is clean and ready to incorporate into the collection. Museums and collectors want the operculum as it is often an important feature in the identification of the shell.

Do not boil shells which are inhabited by hermit crabs. Boiling causes the crab to retreat to the innermost part of the shell where it is difficult to remove. If a shell containing a hermit crab is placed in water which contains a little Clorox, Purex or other bleach, the crab will crawl out and die leaving an empty shell.

Do not upset your neighbors with bad odors. If a shell is difficult to clean completely, there are several options open to you: (a) Bury it for a few days. (b) Put it in formalin for about two days. (c) Put it in alcohol. (d) Soak it in water for an hour and then try again to syringe out the remnants of the animal with a stream of water.

Do not apply varnish or shellac to shells as this ruins them. If you wish to bring out the pattern of a shell or intensify the colors, apply a thin layer of mineral oil (liquid paraffin).

Do not leave shells in bleach (Clorox, Purex) for more than a few hours. The bleach will remove encrustations and the periostracum from the shell. Many collectors deliberately remove the periostracum from shells such as the Cones, but if the shell remains too long in the bleach it will appear "over-cleaned" and "washed-out".

Travelling with shells
If a shell is completely clean and has no odor, it will not create a problem in your suitcase. But if you have not had time for complete cleaning there are several options.

Freeze the mollusc and put it into a wide-mouthed thermos to keep it frozen. Shells can be kept frozen indefinitely without damage.

Place the molluscs in a 95% solution of ethyl alcohol, using a sealed container, plastic, glass or stainless steel.

Soak the shells for a few hours in formalin and then wrap in plastic bags. The shells will smell somewhat of formalin but if wrapped in plastic bags the odor will not be a serious problem.

Storing a shell collection
The way in which one houses a shell collection depends on the space available, one's personal preferences, finances, and the tolerance of one's family! However it needs to be housed in such a way that specimens can be easily located when wanted. Also it needs to be housed in the dark as many shells fade if exposed to light for any length of time. Another important point is that the shells must be labelled or marked in such a way that their identity, place and date of collection, habitat and other information can be indicated.

The most useful method of storing shells is in a cabinet with shallow drawers: these can be obtained from dealers in biological equipment, from shell dealers (see the advertisements in a magazine such as the *Hawaiian Shell News*), made to measure or made by oneself if one is good at carpentry. Drawers about 1½ inches in depth are suitable for most shells; a few deeper drawers or a separate cabinet may be needed for larger specimens. An alternative is stackable boxes, but this is not so convenient.

In the drawers or boxes the individual shells can be put into plastic boxes, glass-topped boxes (many collectors make these themselves by putting glass lids onto ordinary boxes), or plastic or glass phials corked with cottonwool. Mini-clip plastic self-sealing small bags are also handy but do not offer so much protection to their contents. Accompanying the shell should be a label giving its name and other data, or the shell should be numbered in Indian ink and cross-referenced to a filing system.

The operculum, if there is one, must be kept with its shell. Some collectors stick this on a piece of cottonwool and replace it in the shell in the position it would be in life. The snag with this method is that one cannot examine the back surface of the operculum which often has important diagnostic features. An alternative is to put the operculum into the mouth of the shell and plug it with cottonwool.

As the collection grows it will become apparent that some sort of order is necessary if one is to locate a shell quickly. A good method is to keep it in family groups, in an order similar to that in which this book is written.

Many collectors do not realise the need to keep good field records until it is too late. The more information recorded about a shell the better. When observing live specimens in the field notes can be made – there is no need to take and kill many living creatures for the sake of noting where and in what conditions they live. But the more carefully records of time, place and date are kept the more often a pattern of migration and behavior tends to emerge, showing that many molluscs come inshore or go into deeper waters at various times of the year.

How big? Where found? What arrangement?

Shell sizes

Every author who photographs seashells faces the problem of how best to convey to the reader an indication of the shell's actual size. We have tried to cope with this difficulty by giving actual measured sizes with the description of each species. The recorded sizes (usually in millimeters) are actual measurements taken from the largest shells in our collection. It is of course, possible, that the same species in another part of the world could be larger or smaller, since the measured shells all came from Omani waters. Although most sizes are recorded in millimeters, a few of the larger species are recorded in centimeters.

Locality references

A country like Oman, with its many coves and islands, has a coast line of over 1000 miles. The authors have taken samplings of molluscan life at many points along this extensive shore line. Where a given species has been found at most localities studied, a strong probability exists that it inhabits all of Oman's coast, environmental factors permitting. In such cases, we have listed the distribution of the species as *general*, bearing in mind we are referring to Oman only. Where the species has been identified in only a limited area, and there is a high probability that it has a very restricted habitat, the exact locality is identified. The major samplings utilized for this book came from the Musandam peninsula, the Batinah Coast (125 miles of beaches), Sohar, Barka, As Sib, Muscat, Matrah, Qurayat, Sur, Ras Al Hadd, Masirah, the Khuriya Muriya islands, Hasik, Mirbat, Salalah and Raysut.

Systematics

It is convenient to use an established family order when listing molluscs. Therefore, the order of the families in this book are arranged as in Wenz and Zilch, 1938–1961 modified by Taylor and Sohl, 1962, for the gastropods, and R. Moore, 1969, for the bivalves. This is basically the order which is followed in the papers of the Indo-Pacific Mollusca and the order followed by Wagner and Abbott's Standard Catalog of Shells, so it will be familiar to many collectors and students of molluscs.

Subclass **Prosobranchia**
Order **Archeogastropoda**
Class **Gastropoda**

Superfamily **Pleurotomariacea**
Family **Haliotidae (Abalone or Ormer Shells)**
Ear-shaped shells with an almost flat spire; most of the
shell is the body whorl, with a line of holes along one
edge.

Haliotis mariae
Gray, 1831

Interior of shell nacreous and
iridescent, exterior reddish
brown, coarse spiral ridges with
fine lines crossing the ridges. The
holes close up as the animal
grows, leaving six holes open.
Up to 130 mm, those found in
the south of Oman being larger
than those at Muscat.
Distributed generally along the
coastline, it is found clinging to
rocks with its strong muscular
foot. Common. The animals are
vegetarian and feed on algae.

The mother-of-pearl interior
makes attractive costume
jewelry and in some parts of the
world, particularly Japan,
China, New Zealand, California
and the Channel Islands in the
English Channel, the meat is
considered a delicacy.

Superfamily **Fissurellacea**
Family **Fissurellidae (Keyhole Limpets)**
Conical shells with a "keyhole" slit or opening at the
apex in *Diodora* and *Fissurella* but on the anterior part of
the shell or at the edge in other genera, these acting as
an anal aperture for excretory purposes.

Keyhole limpets live attached to rocks, the shape of
the majority of the species being well adapted to
withstand the buffeting of violent waves. They are
usually found low down on the shore or in shallow
water at low tide. They are vegetarian, browsing on
algae, and normally remain stationary during the day,
moving about at night to feed. They are difficult to
remove as they cling tightly to the rocks when danger is
apparent. Therefore if one wishes to collect a living
specimen one must take the mollusc by surprise and
suddenly slip a thin knife blade between its foot and
the rock.

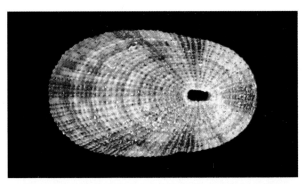

Diodora bombayana
(Sowerby, 1862)

Shell a narrow, rounded oblong,
the apex nearer the anterior, up
to 25 mm, with fine radial
concentric ridges, the interstices
being square in shape. Exterior
white, sometimes rayed with
brown. Interior porcelaneous;
"keyhole" with a truncated callus
surrounding it. Distribution
general. Rare.

Fissurella salebrosa
Reeve, 1850

Shell a flattened cone, apex
nearly central, irregularly oval
and more pointed at the anterior
end, up to 35 mm. Exterior ivory
rayed with brown, coarsely
ridged from the apex to the base.
Interior white, porcelaneous;
"keyhole" with a thickened oval
callus surrounding it. The shell is
arched and will rock like a
rocking chair when placed on a
flat surface, unlike most other
Fissurellidae. Distributed
generally on rocks or in crevices.
Very common.

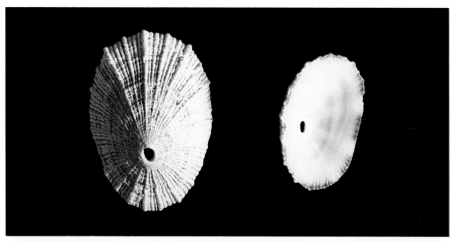

Diodora funiculata
(Reeve, 1850)

Shell similar to *Diodora ruppelli* but not so regular in shape or sculpture, up to 35 mm. There are about three fine ribs between each coarse radial rib. Color white, inside and out, occasionally rayed with brown. Distribution general. Rare.

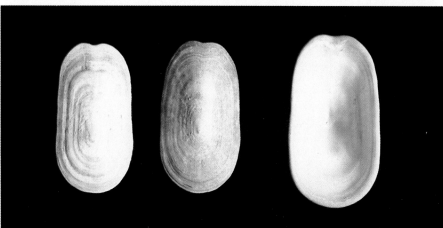

Scutus unguis
(Linnaeus, 1758)

Shell elongate, slightly domed, sides parallel, up to 70 mm. There is an indentation in the anterior margin instead of a slit. The exterior has finely concentric striations, with deeper striations at intervals. Exterior ivory, interior pearly white. Animal black and large, though juveniles are often lighter in color, the mantle covering the shell. Distribution Masirah only. Uncommon.

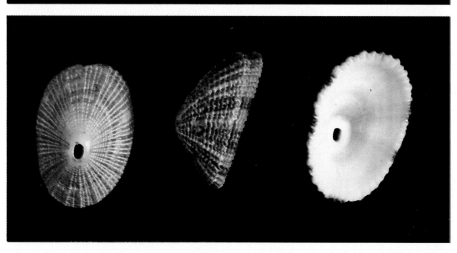

Diodora rueppelli
(Sowerby, 1834)

Shell conical and convex at the posterior, almost concave at the anterior, apex towards the anterior, up to 20 mm. Alternating regular fine and coarse ribs radiating from the apex, crossed by very fine concentric ridges, giving a cancellated appearance. Exterior whitish to ivory, usually rayed with dark brown. Interior white, the callus around the "keyhole" is truncated at the posterior. Distribution general. Uncommon.

Superfamily **Patellacea**
Family **Patellidae (Limpets)**
Circular to oval conical shells with a barely perceptible apex, not coiled, horse-shoe shaped muscle scar. Interior highly glazed.

Limpets (Patellacea) are vegetarian, usually moving about at night to browse on the algae on the rocks. Their shells are perfectly shaped for withstanding the violent action of the waves and they can cling tightly to the rocks, storing water within the shells and thus having the ability to tolerate long periods out of the water, as many live at or near the high tide mark. Comments about collecting live specimens are as for Fissurellacea.

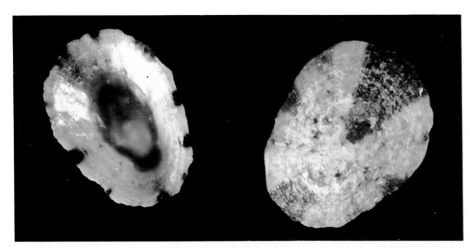

Cellana karachiensis
Winckworth, 1930

Flattish shell, densely ribbed, ribs somewhat granular in appearance, about 20 rather stronger ribs with many weak ones between, up to 55 mm. Exterior brownish with eleven deeper brown rays. Interior highly iridescent and silvery, muscle scar brown often surrounded with a yellow ring, external rays show through to the interior. Distribution general. Common.

Patella exusta pica
Reeve, 1854

Flattish shell with about twenty narrow sharp ribs radiating from the apex with three to four weaker ones between, up to 45 mm. Exterior ivory with radiating dark lines. Interior white bordered with orange-brown, muscle scar the same color. The shell is often encrusted and difficult to see on the rocks. Distribution general. Common.

Family **Acmaeidae**

Characteristics as Patellidae, interior porcelaneous.

Acmaea profunda
Deshayes, 1863

Steeply conical, nearly smooth shells with barely perceptible ribs, up to 21 mm. Exterior ivory, rayed with fine brown lines, edges strongly marked with brown. Interior white, not as shiny as Patella, muscle scar orange to dark brown. Distribution general, common.

Superfamily **Trochacea**
Family **Trochidae (Top Shells)**
Shells top-shaped, sides flat or rounded, base usually
flattened, usually umbilicate. Aperture nearly circular,
operculum horny, spirally coiled and round, closing the
aperture in most cases. Interior of aperture mother-of-
pearl. This nacre often shows through on the exterior if
the shell has been worn or buffeted by wave action. The
animals are vegetarian and feed on algae.

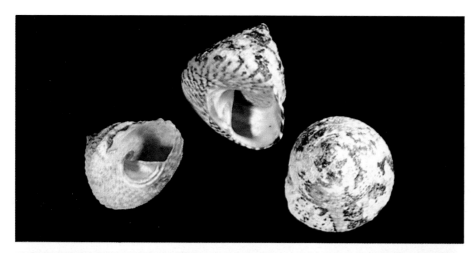

Trochus erythraeus
Brocchi, 1821

Flat-sided, thick heavy shell,
spire height variable, suture
impressed, strongly tuberculate
at shoulder and base of body
whorl, rest of shell ridged and
beaded, up to 44 mm in
diameter. Broad, deep
umbilicus, columella edge
straight and at an angle to the
axis of the shell. Exterior color
variable with streaks of darker
color, usually reddish. Interior of
aperture and umbilicus pearly
white. Distribution general, very
common. Usually found on rocks
in the intertidal zone.

Trochus kochi
Philippi, 1844

Thick, heavy shell with slightly
rounded whorls, impressed
suture and sharply angled keel at
the base, up to 60 mm diameter.
Base smooth, ribbed round the
wide, deep umbilicus. Strong
growth lines follow the angle of
the outer lip, with coarse ribs at
an angle to these. Exterior
whitish with greenish or reddish
zigzag streaks. Umbilicus ridged
within, nacreous, aperture
pearly white within. Distribution
general. Common. Specimens at
Muscat are only about half the
size of those found at Salalah
and Masirah, where it is
particularly common. Easily
found at low tide on rocks.

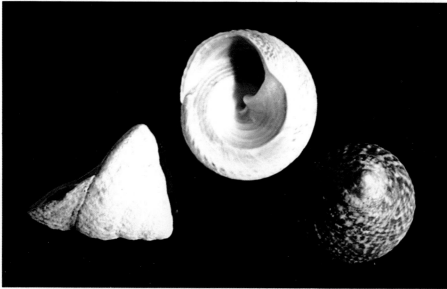

Monilea obscura
(Wood, 1828)

An extremely variable shell, both in shape and color. This species is so variable that it has been given many different names: it has often been called *Monilea kotschyi* Philippi in this region, but the two species intergrade completely in a single area and so the older name is used here. Usually small, but we have found it up to 30 mm in height. Whorls rounded, sometimes angled or tuberculed at the shoulder, Umbilicus small. Columella toothed, sometimes with more than one denticulation. Exterior rough or smooth, whitish variously patterned with greenish, greyish or purplish brown. Aperture greenish mother-of-pearl within.

Distribution general, usually on rocks in the intertidal zone. Uncommon.

Monodonta vermiculata
(Fischer, 1874)

This species has been confused with *Monodonta australis* Lamarck, *Monodonta canalifera* Lamarck and *Monodonta dama* (Philippi). It is less strongly ridged than these and more variably patterned. No umbilicus, inner lip finely grooved, columella terminating in a tooth; the columella has a longitudinal curved groove. Below the tooth is a deep notch.

The illustration shows the variability of patterning and one specimen shows the damage done to the columella by hermit crabs, which chip away parts of the shell to accommodate themselves. This damage has obscured one of the distinguishing characters – the tooth at the bottom of the columella – and could lead to mistakes in identification! Collectors of dead and empty shells need to be aware of this kind of error.
Up to 35 mm in height, found mainly on rocks or in rocky areas. Distribution general, common.

Euchelus atratus
(Gmelin, 1791)

Very similar to *Euchelus asper*, up to 18 mm. More colorful, reddish to dark grey mottled with white, sculpture more pronounced, umbilicus more distinct. Inside of outer lip more grooved. It is probable that those two species are extreme forms of one variable species (*Euchelus asper*). Distribution general, common, usually on rocks.

Euchelus asper
(Gmelin, 1791)

Small, spirally ridged shell, up to 25 mm. Dark grey rounded whorls, the alternately fine and coarse ridges crossed with longitudinal grooves. Columella with a slight tooth, lower edge of lip finely denticulate, umbilicus a chink. *Euchelus proximus* A. Adams is a synonym. Distribution general, common, usually found in sandy pockets between rocks in shallow water.

Clanculus pharaonius
(Linnaeus, 1758)

Sometimes called the "Strawberry Top Shell" because of its obvious resemblance to a strawberry. Rounded whorls, ridged and beaded, red with black markings, up to 28 mm. Distribution general, common, usually found in sandy pockets between rocks in shallow water by goggling, on or underneath rocks. Sometimes we have found them on sand between rocks. These attractive little shells are always popular with collectors.

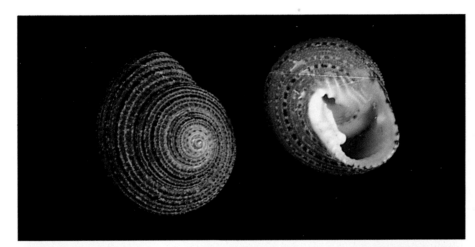

Clanculus puniceus
(Philippi, 1846)

Similar to *Clanculus pharaonius*, but the whorls are less rounded, the suture less well-defined, the sculpture much finer with the two rows of black gemmules being more numerous, less coarse and not interspaced with white. The umbilicus is narrower and the outer lip has a tooth inside the upper margin instead of a bifurcating ridge. Up to 25 mm. Found in the south of Oman, uncommon.

Umbonium vestiarium
(Linnaeus, 1758)

Flattened smooth little shells, up to 15 mm across, umbilicus closed by a thick callus. Glossy and extremely variable in color and patterning. This species lives in sand in shallow water and can be found by the thousand along the Batinah coast at low tide. Distribution general, very common.

Minolia gradata
Sowerby, 1895

Shell small, up to 8 mm in height, whorls spirally sculptured with sharp ridges, the interspaces being wide and very finely diagonally striate. Shoulders flattened. Both the base and the wide deep umbilicus have close, rounded ridges. Columella lip sharply angled, interior of aperture smooth. Color white, patterned with brown (pinkish in worn specimens). Distribution general, common.

Family **Stomatellidae (False Ear Shells)**
Spire flattened, body whorl and aperture large.
Operculum horny.

Stomatella elegans
Gray, 1847

Similar to Abalone Shells but
without the row of holes.
Exterior finely ridged, mottled
with grey, interior brilliantly
nacreous with a bluish tinge, up
to 20 mm. Distribution general,
found clinging to rocks in the
intertidal zone. Uncommon.

Family **Turbinidae (Turban Shells)**

Solid, top-shaped, globose shells, aperture smooth
mother-of-pearl. Operculum calcareous, flat on the
inner side where it is attached to the animal's foot and
convex on the exterior. The operculi have been called
"cat's eyes" and were popular as jewelry in Victorian
times. Animals are vegetarian.

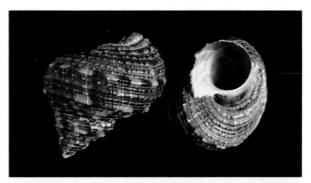

Turbo brunneus
Roeding, 1798

Strong, heavy, spirally corded
shell, up to 60 mm in height.
Umbilicus narrow. Exterior
patterned in brown and cream.
Inner lip and columella white,
interior pearly white.

We have found this only at
Salalah and Masirah where it is
common on rocks in the
intertidal zone.

Turbo radiatus
Gmelin, 1791

A strong, heavy shell, up to 75
mm in height. Encircled by
coarse ridges, crossed by fine
striae, the ridges being beaded or
having spiky projections, those
at the shoulder and base of the
body whorl being particularly
strong. Interior of outer lip white
edged with brown, columella
white, interior pearly white.
Exterior patterned with brown
and cream, a cream band at the
base of the body whorl. The size
range of adults of this species is
very great. Distribution from the
Straits of Hormuz to Ras Al
Hadd. Common at Muscat.

A smaller variety of this
species is found at Salalah and
Masirah, up to 50 mm. The
sculpture is much finer and
smoother and it is uncommon.

Turbo coronatus
Gmelin, 1791

A flat-spired shell, up to 40 mm
across. Whorls moderately
rounded with more or less
marked tubercules or
coronations at the shoulder.
Columella white, interior of
aperture sometimes greenish
nacre, operculum slightly
granular and tinged with green
on the exterior. Distribution
general. Common in the
intertidal range.

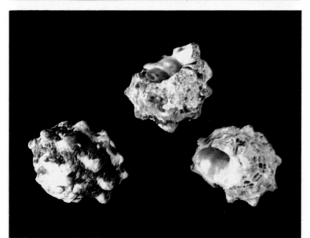

Superfamily **Neritacea**
Family **Neritidae**

Solid globular shells with few whorls and a large body whorl, spire depressed. Columella flattened, broad and shelf-like, aperture semi-circular, operculum calcareous and thick with a peg-like projection which fits into a groove within the aperture and locks it into place. Vegetarian.

Nerites live in the intertidal zone, frequently way above the normal high tide level. They have the ability, common to most intertidal molluscs, to store water within their shells and hence can stand long periods of desiccation. This can be demonstrated if the animal is forcibly pulled away from the rock at which time it will squirt out water as it retracts into the shell.

The unusual peg-like tooth locks the operculum into place: it is almost impossible to remove the operculum from a living specimen and it is often difficult to remove it even when the animal has been dead for some time.

Nerita albicilla
(Linnaeus, 1758)

Finely ribbed, the ribs being flattened and close together and crossed by growth lines, up to 25 mm. Color and pattern variable, some shells being black or dark, and some variously rayed with reddish or dark stripes. Inner lip denticulate, columella shelf yellowish and pustulose, outer lip denticulate within. Operculum granular. Distribution general, common.

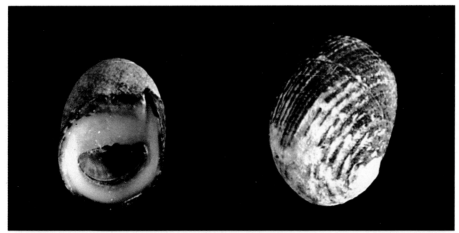

Nerita adenensis
Mienis, 1978

Similar to *Nerita albicilla*, but with a smooth columella shelf, and a very smooth, glassy operculum. The exterior of the shell is variously colored and patterned from orange to brown to grey or black. Up to 20 mm. Distribution probably general, but to date we have found it only in the vicinity of Muscat.

Nerita longii
(Recluz, 1842)

Very globose, flatly ridged shell of few whorls, color usually light brown to black. Columella coarsely ridged and denticulate, white to yellow. Operculum granulose, up to 35 mm. Distribution general on rocks, common.

Nerita textilis
(Gmelin, 1791)

A synonym is *Nerita plexa* Dillwyn. Coarsely ribbed with cord-like ribs crossed by growth lines, up to 50 mm. Exterior white or cream flecked with dark grey or black. Inner edge of aperture denticulate, columella shelf and operculum granular, outer lip denticulate within. Distribution general. Common.

Order **Mesogastropoda**

Superfamily **Cerithiacea**
Family **Turritellidae (Turret Shells)**
Long, slender shells with a circular aperture and a
horny operculum. They are vegetarian, feeding on
detritus in the sand. Because of the slenderness of the
spire, the tips are often broken. Dead shells are common
on the beaches, mostly in a worn condition which
makes identification difficult.

There are several species of Turritella in Oman, but
as they are usually found only in a very poor condition,
definite identification of at least three species has not
proved possible.

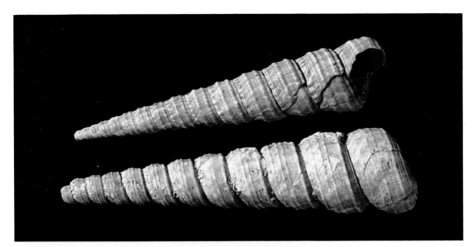

Turritella torulosa
Kiener, 1843–44

A heavier, stronger shell than
Turritella cochlea and
proportionately broader in
relation to its length. The
sculpture is similar but much
coarser and the color of fresh
shells is generally lighter and
more diffuse. Up to 120 mm.
Distribution general. Common,
dead.

Turritella cochlea
Reeve, 1849

A slender, light-weight shell,
with a fine, glassy apex (if
present). The whorls are
encircled by three very fine
sharp ridges, the center one
being weaker than the other
two. The base of the last whorl is
sharply keeled and violet in color
in fresh specimens. The color
pattern is dark brown on lighter
brown, but worn specimens are
paler. Up to 55 mm.
Distribution general. Common,
We have only found this species
cast up, dead.

Family **Architectonicidae (Sundial Shells)**

Flat-based, low conical shells, usually with a wide and very deep umbilicus; operculum horny, usually with a tubercular knob on the inner aspect.

The common name "Sundial Shells" is appropriate as the shells are almost perfectly round and have regular markings reminiscent of a sundial's face. Because of their striking sculpture and color, few shells are as photogenic as these. The final shape of the shell is determined by the way it develops; the coiling of the growing shell occurs in such a way that each whorl is placed above the periphery of the preceding one. The end result of this coiling is the circular shell with an open, deep umbilicus which resembles a spiral staircase. Some authors use the name "Solarium" instead of "Architectonica".

These are sand-dwelling molluscs and their dead, empty shells are often cast up on the beaches.

Architectonica laevigata
(Lamarck, 1816)

Shell a circular flattened cone, up to 35 mm in diameter. Suture distinct, the last whorl having a narrow, flat ridge, a broad ridge and then two narrow ones, divided by fine incised lines. Keel sharp. Base with two narrow, flat ridges around the circumference and two beaded ones around the umbilicus. Color purplish-cream, with brownish blotches on the narrow ridges and fine broken brown lines on the wide one. Distribution general, uncommon.

Architectonica perspectiva
(Linnaeus, 1758)

More depressed than
Architectonica laevigata up to 60
mm. Sculpture of the last whorl
as in *Architectonica laevigata*, but
the basal ridge is narrower. The
whorls are axially incised with
fine lines on the upper half.
Upper ridge, top of wide ridge
and next narrow ridge marked
with squarish brown blotches on
mushroom background. Base
paler with fine brown dots on
the outer ridges and round the
umbilicus.
Distribution general. Common.

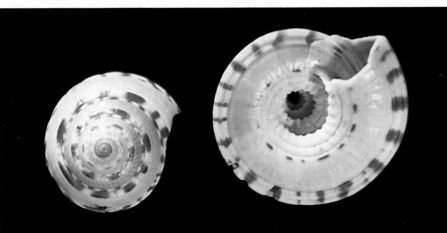

Architectonica purpurata
(Hinds, 1844)

Similar to the first named above,
flatter, up to 40 mm. The last
whorl is divided into five more or
less equally wide flat ridges, the
top and the last two being
blotched with brown. The
umbilicus is bordered by two
very fine and one wide beaded
ridge, the latter being almost
strongly ribbed or toothed rather
than beaded. Upper whorls
cancellate in appearance.
Distribution general.
Uncommon.

Heliacus variegatus
(Gmelin, 1791)

A small shell up to 15 mm,
spirally corded and patterned
light and dark brown. Umbilicus
very deep and narrow.
Operculum horny with a conical
projection on the inner surface.
Distribution general, can be
found in sand at low tide,
common.

Family **Vermetidae**

The animal is closely related to the Turritellas and
Sundials, but instead of growing in symmetrical whorls
the mollusc twists and contorts so that a completely
haphazard shape develops, in the form of a shelly tube.

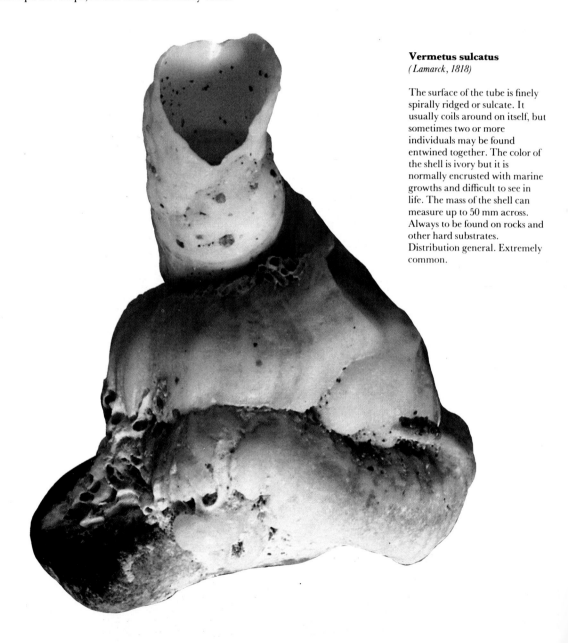

Vermetus sulcatus
(Lamarck, 1818)

The surface of the tube is finely
spirally ridged or sulcate. It
usually coils around on itself, but
sometimes two or more
individuals may be found
entwined together. The color of
the shell is ivory but it is
normally encrusted with marine
growths and difficult to see in
life. The mass of the shell can
measure up to 50 mm across.
Always to be found on rocks and
other hard substrates.
Distribution general. Extremely
common.

Family **Planaxidae**

Thick, conical-globose shells, no umbilicus. There is a
slight anterior canal and a thin, horny operculum.
Often the tip of the spire is worn off.

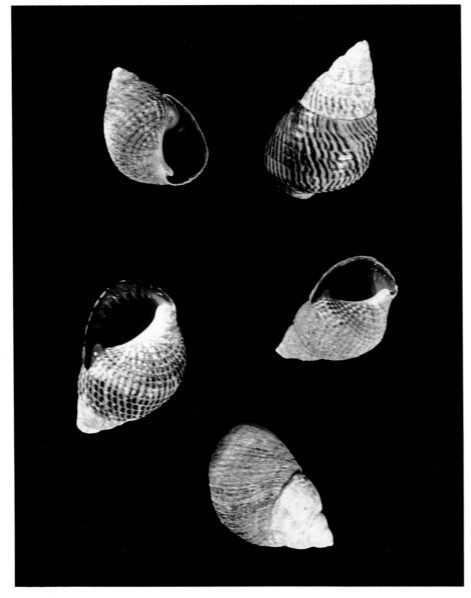

Planaxis sulcatus
(Born, 1778)

A strong heavy shell up to 30
mm. Spirally corded and dark
grey or greenish grey, aperture
purple-brown within.
Frequently found in large
numbers high in the intertidal
zone on rocks at the edge of
pools. Distribution general,
common.

Family **Modulidae**

Flattened globose shells with a tooth-like projection on the columella.

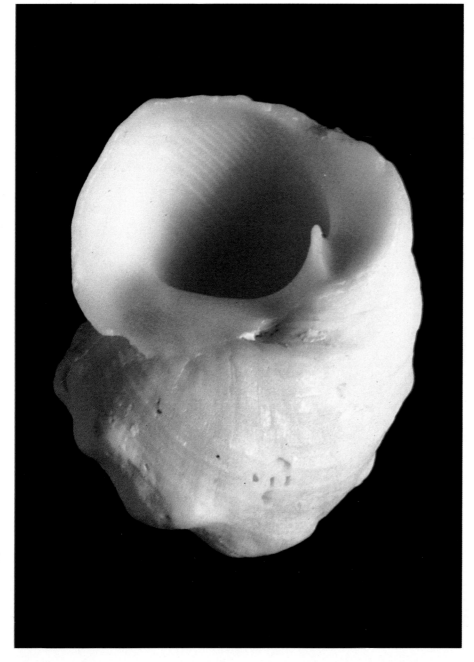

Modulus tectum
(Gmelin, 1791)

A solid shell with a depressed spire. Globose and white in color with a white aperture and columella. Operculum corneus, thin, circular. Up to 30 mm. Found living in sand in shallow water. This northern Indian Ocean form is unusual in the all-white columella, which is normally marked with brown.

Family **Potamididae**

Elongated shells, usually thick and heavy for their size, with a twisted columella, short anterior canal and often an expanded outer lip. Operculum horny. The shells in this family are often called Horn Shells or Mud Snails. Habitat is usually muddy creeks or mangrove swamps.

Cerithidea cingulata
(Gmelin, 1791)

Shell elongated, up to 45 mm. Three rows of noduled ridges per whorl. Outer lip expanded, white within. Shell brownish.

This species is present by the tens of thousands in some creeks and estuarine areas. It is so plentiful in some areas that one can pick up at least 25 in one handful. The Marine Biologists of Aramco in Saudi Arabia have designated one elevation of the beach and mud flats at Tarut Bay "The Cerithidea Zone" because of the abundance of these molluscs at that level. It is generally distributed and extremely common in Oman.

Telescopium telescopium
(Linnaeus, 1758)

Very elevated, heavy, conical, brown shell, up to 80 mm. It reminds one of the ancient descriptions of the Tower of Babel. We have found it only near Muscat, dead. Very rare.

Terebralia palustris
(Linnaeus, 1767)

A large, heavy, coarsely ridged brown shell, up to 120 mm. Outer lip expanded, interior brown. This species lives in the shallow water of the mud flats which get sea water only during high tide. The swamps of Qurm Creek support thousands of these shells. They eat detritus in the mud. Distribution general in swamps and creeks, very common.

Family **Cerithiidae**

Elongate shells with an anterior canal and a posterior notch. The operculum is horny. Many species are sculptured with tubercules, nodules, spiral cords or axial ribs. They are a shallow water family which feed on plant detritus and algae. They are variable in size, shape and sculpture and often are very confusing to the amateur and others.

Cerithium columna
Sowerby, 1830

White to cream shell, up to 55 mm, marked variously with darker color. Shell spirally ridged, ridges rough and turberculed sharply at the shoulder. Anterior canal long and twisted. Usually found in sand in the intertidal zone. Distribution general. Uncommon.

Clypeomorus bifasciatus
(Sowerby, 1855)

A small, finely tuberculate shell, up to 20 mm, with rounded whorls and ill-defined sutures. Inside of outer lip finely denticulate and marked with brown dashes. Anterior canal very short. Two color forms are to be found: one banded white and brown and the other blackish with darker tubercules. This species lives in the intertidal zone, often high on the shore on rocks or in silty sand with a hard substrate. Distribution general. Common.

Cerithium pingue
A. Adams, 1855

Small brown ceriths, up to
18 mm in height, characterized
by the constriction of the body
whorl above the mouth. The
operculum is oval and
completely fills the aperture.
Distribution general.
Uncommon. Found at low tide
on sand or on seaweeds

Cerithium caeruleum
Sowerby, 1855

Shell heavy for its size, up to
40 mm, encircled with a row of
large blunt dark-colored nodules
with rows of smaller coarse
nodules and ridges between.
Exterior black and white, outer
lip and columella white, interior
of mouth pale or darkish,
anterior canal short and wide.
Distribution general, usually on
or near rocks. Very common.

Cerithium scabridum
Philippi, 1848

A small, up to 22 mm, white
shell, dotted with dark color.
There is a noticeable channel
between the whorls which are
sculptured with spiral rows of
beaded ridges. Anterior canal
very short. Distribution general
but most likely to be found in the
intertidal zone on the Batinah
coast beaches near Muscat,
though it can often be found on
rocks or silt as well as sand. It
can be distinguished from
Clypeomorus bifasciatus (with
which it is often confused) by the
distinct channelled sutures
between the whorls. Very
common.

Cerithium nodulosum
erythraeonense
Lamarck, 1822

Large and comparatively heavy,
up to 65 mm. Sculpture
moderately coarse with blunt
nodules and spiral incised lines.
Outer lip expanded, finely
denticulate and white within,
not projecting across the anterior
canal, which is short. This
subspecies differs from *Cerithium
nodulosum* in its smaller size, finer
sculpture and the lack of the
projection of the outer lip across
the anterior canal. We have
found it only at Masirah where it
is uncommon, frequently
exposed in the intertidal zone on
muddy, silty flats.

Rhinoclavis fasciata
(Bruguière, 1792)

Long, smooth shell, up to 75 mm, very faint axial and spiral lines, exterior cream, marbled with light brown, columella and interior of mouth white. Anterior canal long and bent sharply backwards, one columellar fold. Often found in the intertidal zone on sandy or silty mud flats. Distribution general. Uncommon.

Rhinoclavis sinensis
(Gmelin. 1791)

Wider in proportion to its height than *Rhinoclavis fasciata*, up to 50 mm. Whorls rounded, sculptured with fine spiral cords, tuberculate at the shoulder. Cream mottled with brown blotches and spots, brown blotch on columella, interior of aperture white, sometimes lined with brown. The sculpture is variable, some specimens being more or less prominently tuberculed than others. We have found it at Salalah, Sur, Muscat and Masirah. Common.

Rhinoclavis kochi
(Philippi, 1848)

Slender shell, up to 45 mm, the specimens found at Masirah being much larger than those found at Muscat. Shiny, beaded appearance, with varices on each whorl, a strong one being opposite the outer lip. Brown incised lines between the beaded ridges. Anterior canal long and bent sharply backwards, posterior canal weak. Interior of mouth and columella white. Distribution general. Common.

Superfamily **Epitoniacea (Scalacea)**
Family **Epitoniidae (Scalidae) (Wentletraps)**
Elongate shells with varices or varix-like ribs, and
circular apertures. Sometimes umbilicate. Operculum
round and horny. Found burrowing in the sand at low
tide.

Epitonium pallasii
(Kiener, 1838)

A moderately large, delicate
shell, broad in comparison with
its height, with eleven to twelve
varices per whorl. Ivory or
brown in color, with white
varices. The umbilicus is deep.
Up to 65 mm. Distribution
general. Rare.

Epitonium aculeatum
(Sowerby, 1844)

Small, white, sometimes flushed with brown, more elongate than the above, varices sharp, not umbilicate. Shell surface smooth between the varices. Up to 25 mm. Distribution general. Uncommon.

Epitonium fimbriolatum
(Melvill, 1897)

White with very fine delicate varices, close set and projecting above the shoulders of the whorls. In beach worn specimens these projections are often worn down. Up to 70 mm. Found in sand at low tide. Distribution general. Rare.

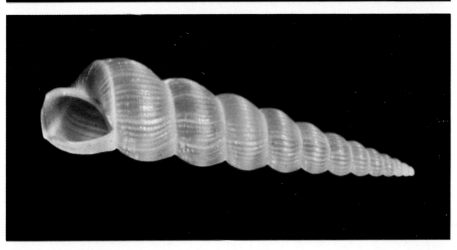

Amaea acuminata
(Sowerby, 1844)

Very elongate brown shell with extremely fine longitudinal ribs and a marked ridge at the base of the body whorl. The whorls are encircled by a lighter brown band. Up to 30 mm. Distribution general. Uncommon.

Family **Janthinidae (Violet snails)**

Fragile, globose shells with a wide aperture and no operculum. The animals are pelagic, and spend their lives afloat on the open ocean, drifting effortlessly suspended from a raft of air bubbles formed by mucus secreted by the animals. They live in colonies and the floating rafts also serve as egg cradles. They eat other floating organisms in the plankton. If the animal is torn off the raft, which occasionally happens when the seas are stormy, it can not swim and will sink and die.

Janthina janthina
(Linnaeus, 1758)

Shell flattish and keeled, purple above and paler below. Up to 40 mm. Found washed up on the beaches. Distribution general. Uncommon.

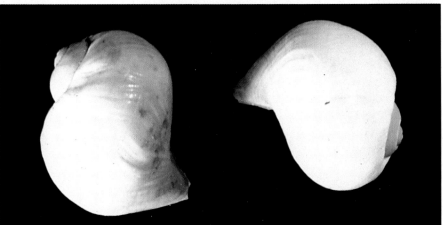

Janthina globosa
Swainson, 1822

More globose than *Janthina janthina* and more uniformly violet colored. Up to 35 mm. Found washed up after storms. Distribution general. Uncommon.

Superfamily **Melanellacea (Eulimacea)**
Family **Melanellidae**
Small smooth conical pointed shells, usually without a
radula but with a sucking apparatus which suits their
normally parasitic mode of life. Some species live upon
other forms of life and some are parasitic within their
host.

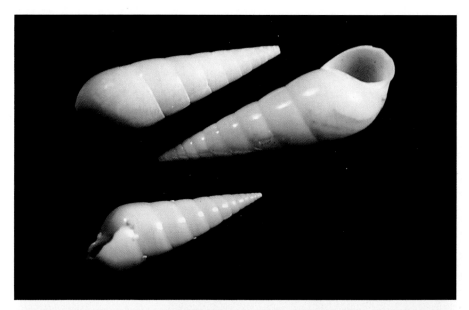

Melanella cumingii
(A. Adams, 1854)

An elegantly shaped marble-
white shell, very smooth and
polished, slightly twisted over at
the apex. It has a small, white
corneous operculum. Up to 40
mm. It is reputedly carnivorous,
eating such creatures as sea stars
and sand dollars. Distribution
general. Rare.

Niso venosa
Sowerby, 1895

A delicately marked little
shining shell, brown on ivory,
umbilicate, with a thin corneous
operculum. Found crawling just
under the surface of the sand.
Up to 15 mm. Distribution
general. Uncommon.

Superfamily **Hipponicacea (Amaltheacea)**
Family **Vanikoridae**
Globular low-spired shells with an umbilicus and an
operculum.

Vanikoro cancellata
(Lamarck , 1822)

A finely cancellate white shell;
animal white also. Up to 20 mm
A sand dweller, feeding upon
detritus. Distribution general.
Rare.

Superfamily **Calyptraecea**
Family **Calyptraeidae (Cup and Saucer shells)**
Conical shells with almost central apex and an internal
shelf or projection, hence the name "cup and saucer
shell".

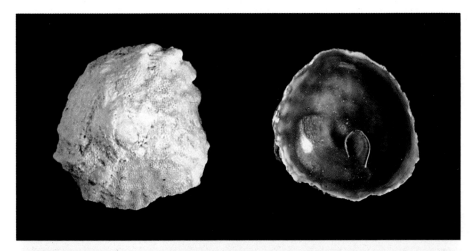

Calyptraea edgariana
Melvill, 1898

Shell a flattish cone, somewhat
irregular in shape. Exterior ivory
to violet, interior shiny, the color
varying from pale to very deep
purple or brownish purple. The
internal projection is somewhat
spoon-shaped. Up to 25 mm in
diameter. The animal lives
attached to a rock or another
shell, and is a filter feeder,
extracting its food from the
water circulating through the
gill apparatus. Although limpet-
like in appearance it is not a true
limpet. Distribution general.
Common.

Cheilea cicatrosa
(Reeve, 1858)

A coarse whitish somewhat
corrugated irregular conical
shell with a white interior and an
internal conical projection open
at one side. Up to 35 mm. Found
living on rocks or other molluscs.
Distribution general. Rare.

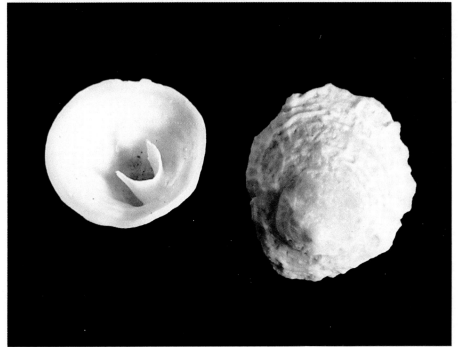

Superfamily **Strombacea**
Family **Xenophoridae (Carrier Shells)**
Few shells deserve their names as aptly as do the Carrier Shells, the Latin name *Xenophora* meaning "Carriers of Strangers". These flattened top-shaped shells attach fragments of stones, coral, shells, etc. to their exterior as they grow, creating a perfect camouflage; on the sea-bed they look like ordinary rubble and would no doubt be passed-up by even a ravenously hungry fish. Some species collect only stones, while others collect shell fragments or other objects. Beyond the shadow of a doubt the Carrier Shells were the first genuine shell collectors, and their camouflage is so good that one might almost imagine that the little animal, snug in its shell, is capable of having a good chuckle to itself while a school of fish are hunting nearby!

Xenophora corrugata
(Reeve, 1843)

A low conical shell with a cream colored base, radially and spirally ridged, and no umbilicus. Operculum thin and corneous. The majority of attachments are shell fragments. Up to 60 mm in diameter. Distribution general, uncommon.

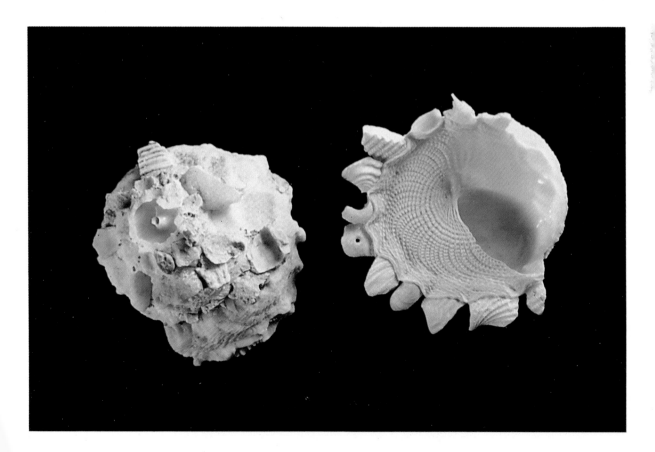

Family **Strombidae**

Heavy, low spired shells with anterior canal; body
whorl usually large and the outer lip flared or with
projections. All have the "stromboid notch" more or less
strongly indented near the anterior through which the
animal can protrude the tentacle bearing an eye. The
genus Strombus has a saw-edged horny operculum, the
other members of the family have smooth edged
operculi.

The operculum is functionally employed to assist the
animal in movement; it moves in a series of lurches,
accomplished by using the operculum to dig into the
sand and provide a purchase at the outer limit of the
extended foot, then, by a sudden contraction of the
muscles of the foot the shell lurches forward. They also
use the operculum to right themselves if they are
accidentally over-turned. All are herbivorous.

Strombus plicatus sibbaldi
Sowerby, 1842

A subspecies of *Strombus plicatus*
(Roeding), shell pale and often
without any colored patterning,
shoulders strongly tuberculate
and upper whorls longitudinally
ribbed. Interior of outer lip
white, columella ridged and
sometimes marked with brown.
Up to 45 mm. Distribution
general. Rare.

Strombus fusiformis
Sowerby, 1842

Shell cream to ivory, faintly patterned with brown, ridged on the lower (anterior) part of the body whorl and within the aperture and on the columella. There are a few low knobs on the shoulder. Up to 50 mm. Distribution general. Rare.

Strombus gibberulus
Linnaeus, 1758

Shell brownish in color, sometimes with a brown line below the suture. Interior of outer lip pink to purple. The pink interior, characteristic of the Red Sea subspecies *Strombus gibberulus albus*, is quite often found in the Indian Ocean species, but they lack the very pale body color of the Red Sea subspecies. The majority of the Omani shells tend to have the pink aperture and it is possible that they tend to merge with or towards the Red Sea shells. Up to 65 mm. Distribution general. Uncommon.

Strombus mutabilis
Swainson, 1821

The smallest Omani species of Strombus, averaging 25 mm in height. It has an unusually wide color variation, sometimes being completely orange, sometimes brown and sometimes multicolored with stripes. Unlike most members of the family it is frequently found among rocks where it lives on rock ledges or in the sand between rocks. Up to 40 mm. Distribution general. Very common.

Strombus oldi
Emerson, 1965

The largest Strombus found in
Oman, shell thick and heavy
with a pronounced flaring outer
lip and strikingly patterned with
brown on the body whorl.
Interior of outer lip and
columella ivory to cream. Up to
130 mm. It has been found at an
inhabited island off the southern
coast of Oman and is very rare.
It has only been recently
described by Dr. Emerson of the
American Museum of Natural
History and is named after Mr.
William E. Old, Jr. who has
made a major contribution to
this book by assisting in the
identification of many of the
species. It has been found in
sand at depths of between six to
twenty feet at low tide.

Strombus decorus persicus
Swainson, 1821

A subspecies of *Strombus decorus
decorus*, lacking the shoulder
tubercules, with the interior of
the lip more commonly white
and the patterning on the body
whorl being less pronounced. Up
to 65 mm. Distribution general.
Very common in sand at or
below the low tide mark.

Lambis truncata sebae
Kiener, 1843

The giant member of this family extending up to 350 mm in height, is often called the Spider Conch. The spire is low but pointed, not blunt as in the similar *Lambis truncata truncata* and the shell is somewhat heavier in comparison with that species. Body whorl is brown patterned with darker brown and the columella and interior of the aperture is pink to purplish or orange to yellowish in color. Distribution is general throughout Oman, in sand but almost always found near large rocks, grazing on algae at depths of one to twelve feet below the surface. The operculum is corneous and strong, usually measuring about 70 mm in length.

Strombus decorus decorus
(Roeding, 1798)

Low-spired cream colored shells with brown ornamentation in bands. Tubercles on the shoulder. Interior of outer lip tinged with pink or salmon pink. Up to 75 mm. Distribution in Oman is confined to Masirah, where they are to be found at or below the low tide level. Common.

Terebellum terebellum
(Linnaeus, 1758)

A torpedo-shaped shell up to 70 mm with a long aperture, almost three quarters the length of the shell. The color patterns are extremely variable, sometimes being spotted, other times striped or checked. The exterior is always glossy and shiny. The animal is herbivorous. It lives in shallow water on a sandy substrate. Distribution general. Uncommon.

Tibia insulaechorab curta
Sowerby, 1842

This is a thick chunky species up to 200 mm in length, with a short straight siphonal canal. Often the tip of the canal or the spire are broken off so that perfect specimens are hard to find. Most shells are coffee-brown in color and the operculum is long, narrow and thin. Specimens have been collected in off-shore sand but they have also been dredged at depths of up to 100 feet. Distribution general. Uncommon.

Superfamily **Cypraeacea**
Family **Cypraeidae**

Smooth glossy ovoid or cylindrical shells with a barely
perceptible spire and a long, narrow aperture on the
base of the shell, more or less strongly toothed on both
edges. No operculum. Herbivorous. An unusual
characteristic of this family among molluscs is that the
females brood over their egg masses until they hatch.
The veliger larvae develop into thin-shelled, Oliva-like
animals and the typical thick shell and toothed aperture
develops only at the adult stage. There is considerable
variation in the size of the adults within a species, even
in the same locality. In general, however, those
specimens found at Masirah tend to be larger than
those found further north.

The so-called "teeth" are called such only because of
their strong resemblance to mammalian teeth. They do
not function for purposes of mastication, but rather, are
thought to be "mantle guides".

Cowries move about (usually at night) by muscular
contractions in the foot. The contractions are so well
synchronized that the cowry can literally turn on the
spot.

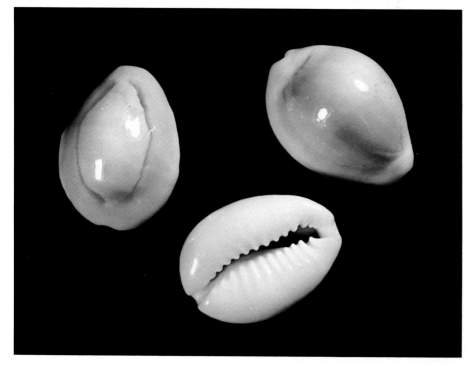

Cypraea annulus
Linnaeus, 1758

Shell small and solid, flattish,
cream colored with an orange
ring around the dorsum. Up to
30 mm. Animal has a greyish-
black mantle with yellow-grey
papillae and a dark grey foot.
We have found this species at
Salalah and Masirah in shallow
water, usually under rocks or
rubble. Rare.

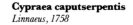

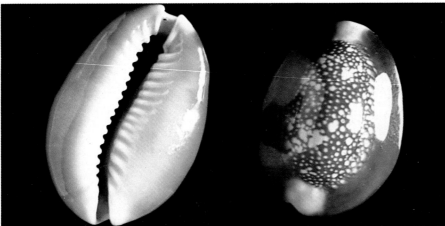

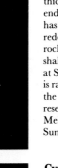

Cypraea caputserpentis
Linnaeus, 1758

Dorsum spotted with light cream or bluish spots on brown, margins deep brown and thickened, pale blotches at each end. Up to 38 mm. The animal has a greenish-brown foot and reddish-brown mantle. It is a rock dweller, usually found in shallow water. We have found it at Salalah and Masirah where it is rare, though it is common in the Indo-Pacific generally It resembles *Cypraea caputdraconis* Melvill and *Cypraea englerti* Summers and Burgess.

Cypraea carneola
Linnaeus, 1758

Shell pinkish, banded with deeper color and with mauve between the teeth, up to 70 mm. Some authors consider the Northern Indian Ocean species to belong to the subspecies *Cypraea carneola crassa* Gmelin. The animal has a grey foot, cream below and a dark greyish-brown mantle with branched papillae. Distribution general, common, and can be found at low tide in rock crevices and under stones or in the branches of coral.

Cypraea caurica
Linnaeus, 1758

This shell is extremely variable, giving rise to many so-called 'races' or subspecies. It is patterned with blotches and spots of brown on a grey or greenish background; the edge of the shell is pinkish with dark spots. Up to 65 mm, those found at Masirah are usually larger than those found at Muscat. A rock dweller, common at Masirah but uncommon elsewhere in Oman.

Cypraea felina fabula
Kiener, 1846

A greenish shell mottled with darker color, yellow sides and base with large dark spots on the margins. This Erythraean subspecies is more globose and darker than the typical *Cypraea felina* Gmelin which is not found in Oman. Up to 28 mm. The animal has a grey foot and dark grey-black mantle. Distribution general. Common.

Cypraea gangranosa
Dillwyn, 1817

A small greyish shell with large white spots on the dorsum, sometimes with brown "eyes" in them, and reddish brown underneath at the ends. Up to 38 mm. The animal has a brown foot and brownish-black mantle. We have found it at Muscat, Salalah and Masirah beneath rocks in shallow water. Rare.

Cypraea chinensis
Gmelin, 1791

A pale shell, up to 48 mm, characterized by the orange-red between the teeth and purple-spotted base and margins. The animal has a reddish foot and darker red mantle. We have found it at Salalah and Masirah, under rocks. Rare.

Cypraea clandestina
Linnaeus, 1767

A small pale, usually creamy-white shell, faintly banded with slightly darker color, up to 25 mm. The foot is black and the mantle grey-black. We have found several living specimens at Muscat, Salalah and Masirah at low tide, up to depths of about six feet. Rare.

Cypraea helvola
Linnaeus, 1758

A small comparatively heavy shell, up to 30 mm, usually with a reddish-brown base and purple ends, the dorsum being spotted with white or cream. The animal has a purple brown foot and mantle. We have found this species only at Salalah and Masirah. Rare.

Cypraea grayana
Schilder, 1930

Some people consider this to be only a form of *Cypraea arabica* Linnaeus. The most prominent distinguishing feature of this shell is its tendency to "humpback". The animal has a grey to black foot and grey-green mantle. Up to 78 mm. Distribution is general, under rocks, in crevices or under rock ledges, often above the low tide level. Very common.

Cypraea gracilis notata
Gill, 1858

A bluish shell, up to 25 mm, those at Masirah being larger than those found at Muscat. The base is slightly spotted with purple, especially at the ends. The foot is reddish-brown and the mantle is truly spectacular with its bright orange-red color and red papillae. Distribution general, under fairly large stones below low tide level, Fairly common.

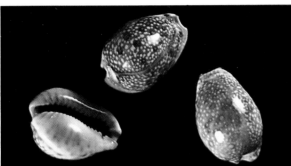

Cypraea marginalis pseudocellata
Schilder and Schilder, 1939

An olive colored shell with white spots, some ringed with brown, and violet dashes on the pale purple margins and base. Up to 35 mm. The animal has a grey foot and grey-brown mantle covered with branched grey-brown papillae. We have found this species only at Salalah and Masirah. Rare.

Cypraea isabella
Linnaeus, 1758

A brownish shell with dark lines on the dorsum and orange ends. Up to 45 mm. The animal has a dark brown-black foot and beautiful jet-black mantle. We have often found it associated with coral, frequently within the branches, but it is also found beneath rocks at low tide. Distribution general. Rare.

Cypraea lentiginosa
Gray, 1825

A small bluish, faintly banded shell, up to 38 mm. The ends of the shell are dark. The foot of the animal is orange-brown and the mantle black. We have found it beneath rocks and coral at Masirah only. Rare.

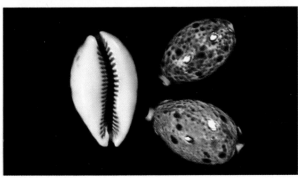

Cypraea lynx
Linnaeus, 1758

A pale shell spotted with brown, up to 65 mm. The foot of the animal is grey-brown and the mantle is grey with long white papillae. Distribution is general but it is rare in Oman.

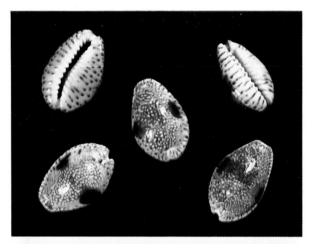

Cypraea nebrites
Melvill, 1888

A humped shell with pale spots on a darker brownish green background. The margins are brown spotted with darker brown and there is a large brown blotch on either side. Up to 40 mm. Foot and mantle of the animal are grey. We have found it in rocky crevices and under stones or in coral, sometimes above the low tide level. Distribution is general. Fairly common.

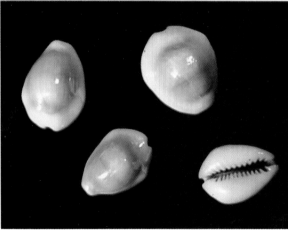

Cypraea moneta
Linnaeus, 1758

The famous "money cowry" which was commonly used for monetary exchange throughout the Indo-Pacific. It is a small, up to 38 mm, bright yellow shell and the animal has a black foot and yellow and black mantle. It is not difficult to imagine an eager suitor trudging hopefully towards the home of a potential father-in-law with a sack of these cowries on his back. We have found this species only at Salalah and Masirah. Rare.

Cypraea mauritiana
Linnaeus, 1758

A large humped shell, up to 110 mm, with a flat base, deep brown margins and spotted dorsum. The animal has a dark foot and almost black mantle. We have found that it tends to live in places exposed to heavy seas, often in crevices, only at the Khuriya Muriya Islands and on the south-eastern coast at Hasik. Although it is common in the Indo-Pacific, it is relatively rare in Oman.

Cypraea ocellata
Linnaeus, 1758

A brownish shell with pale spots, some with "eyes" of purple-black and lighter margins and base, spotted with brown or traces of brown between the coarse teeth. Up to 39 mm. It is well-named because of its ocellated appearance. The foot is grey and the mantle grey-brown. Distribution general in rocky areas. Uncommon.

Cypraea staphylaea
Linnaeus, 1758

A globular shell which gives one 'the impression of a ball. It is dark grey with orange brown teeth on the paler base and dark terminal blotches,. The shell is warty to feel; the animal has a grey-brown foot and brown-black mantle. Up to 26 mm. We have found it only at Salalah and Masirah. Rare.

Cypraea onyx persica
Schilder and Schilder, 1939

Brown base and margins, with a lighter banded dorsum. Up to 65 mm. The foot and mantle of the animal are black. Sometimes we have found it just above low-tide level, under or between rocks.

An unusual feature in this species is its tendency to inhabit broken fragments of larger dead shells. At Mahawt (southern coast of Oman) we found specimens living in pieces of dead *Cardium pseudolima*, *Pecten townsendi* and *Fasciolaria trapezium*. Distribution, the southern coast of Oman from Ras Al Hadd to Salalah and Masirah. Rare.

Cypraea pulchra
Gray, 1824

Few living creatures deserve their name as richly as does this species, "the beautiful cowry". It is light colored, with two distinct black terminal spots at each end; the fishermen refer to it as "Four eyes". The animal has a jet black foot and mantle. Up to 75 mm. In his book, *The Living Cowries*, Dr. C. M. Burgess describes how the habitat of this shell (always associated with branched coral) was found, an elderly blind fisherman leading the way to a cove where he had seen it twenty years previously. Distribution from Muscat to Ras Al Hadd, but we have not found it west of the Ras. Uncommon.

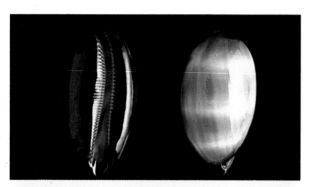

Cypraea talpa
Linnaeus, 1758

A creamy-yellowish shell with dark brown sides and base, up to 90 mm. It resembles *Cypraea exusta* from the Red Sea but the teeth are coarser. The animal has a black foot and grey-black mantle. Distribution probably general. Rare. One living specimen, found at Muscat, was kept in the author's salt-water aquarium for several weeks.

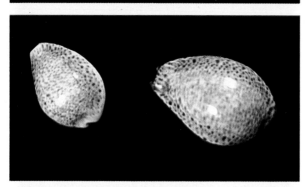

Cypraea vitellus
Linnaeus, 1758

A brownish shell, up to 70 mm, spotted with white and with an off-white base. The sides are characteristically striated, distinguishing it from the similar Red Sea species, *Cypraea camelopardalis* Perry. The animal has a grey foot and grey mantle with long yellow papillae. It is often found in association with *Cypraea grayana* and *Cypraea turdus winckworthi*, the three species often living together under the same rock. Distribution probably general; we have found it to be rare at Muscat but common at Masirah.

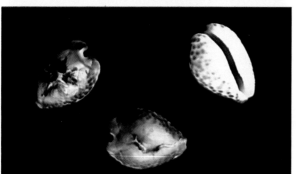

Cypraea turdus winckworthi
Schilder and Schilder, 1939

A greenish shell with a pale base, the dorsum covered with small brown spots. The color is extremely variable and some specimens are quite pale, almost white. The animal has a grey foot and greenish-grey mantle with long papillae, making it look like a bush in the water, an excellent camouflage. At low tide it can be found in crevices and beneath small rocks. Up to 55 mm. Distribution general, very common. It is the commonest cowry found in Oman. In recent years, specimens have been found which show melanism, the cause of this blackness being unknown.

Cypraea teuleri
Cazenavette, 1846

An irregularly shaped greyish shell with dark distinctive dorsal markings and often a deep dorsal sulcus or groove. Up to 67 mm. This species is unusual in this family in that it lacks columellar teeth. The animal has a reddish brown foot and pale orange mantle. It lives in sandy-sludgy areas where there is plenty of seaweed often being exposed to the air at low tide. Because of the sandy environment grains of sand often get into the mantle and cause scarring on the shell surface. It is confined to Masirah and a few places on the neighboring coast of Oman. Until a few years ago it was considered an exceptionally rare shell but now it is known to be common in its limited habitat.

Family **Ovulidae**

Similar to cowries but with the ends expanded and the
teeth on the aperture not so marked.

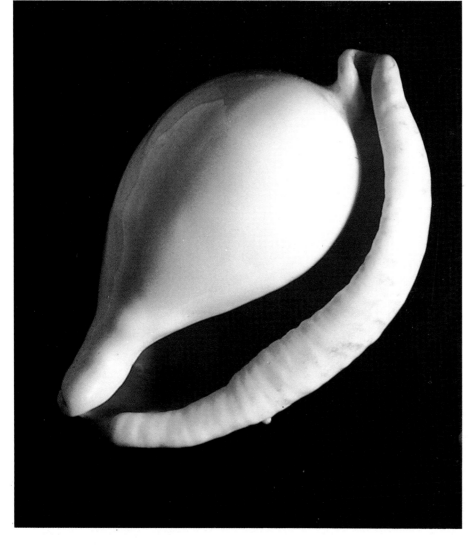

Ovula ovum
(Linnaeus, 1758)

The shells of this family are often
called "egg shells" because of
their resemblance to chicken's
eggs. This species is white and
glossy, like porcelain. The
columellar teeth are absent. The
interior is a rich reddish-brown.
Up to 100 mm. The animal has a
black foot and a jet-black mantle
with golden yellow papillae
which is very beautiful. Dead
shells have been found at Muscat
and Masirah, but the first living
specimen of which we know was
found in June 1979, in about
twenty feet of water at Fahal
Island off Muscat, resting on a
piece of coral, by Mr. Noel
Pettigrew.

Superfamily **Naticacea**
Family **Naticidae (Moon Shells or Necklace Shells)**
Globular shells, the umbilicus sometimes open,
sometimes closed partially or completely by a callus,
operculum either shelly or horny. The animals are
powerful, with a shovel-shaped muscular foot with
which to plow their way through the sand. Some species
are unable to withdraw completely into their shells. All
are carnivorous, boring holes through the shells of other
molluscs to get at the flesh. Eggs are laid in a gelatinous
collar surrounded on the outside with grains of sand.
These empty collars are sometimes found on the beach,
thrown up by the waves after the eggs have hatched.

Natica alapapilionis
(Roeding, 1798)

Globular brownish shell with
four bands of white marked by
dark squarish blotches.
Umbilicus semilunar. Spire low.
Operculum shelly and thick,
completely closing the aperture.
Up to 25 mm in width.
Distribution general. Dead shells
are common along the Batinah
coast.

Natica gualteriana
Recluz, 1844

Grey-brown shell, white round
the narrow semi-lunar
umbilicus. Interior of aperture
purple-brown, sometimes faintly
banded. Darker lines sometimes
occur on the shoulder or across
the whole of the body whorl. Up
to 32 mm in width. Operculum
calcareous (shelly) and
completely closing the aperture.
Distribution – Masirah only.
Rare.

Natica pulicaris
Philippi, 1851

A synonym is *Natica tincturata* Reeve, 1855. Variously patterned brown on ivory, dark brown bands entering and round the deep circular umbilicus. Interior of aperture faintly tinged with purple. Calcareous operculum. Up to 30 mm. We have found this species only at Masirah. Uncommon.

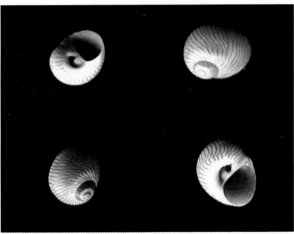

Natica lineata
(Roeding, 1798)

Ivory-colored shell marked with wavy brown lines. Umbilicus deep and ridged. Operculum shelly, spirally ridged, closing the aperture. Up to 22 mm in width. Distribution general, common.

Natica vitellus
(Linnaeus, 1758)

Solid, globular, low-spired shell with a deep umbilicus. The basic off-white color is patterned with orange-brown spiral bands and axial streaks. At the apex the spiral bands converge to a deep purple dot. Aperture white. Operculum calcareous, closing the aperture. Up to 22 mm. Distribution general. Uncommon.

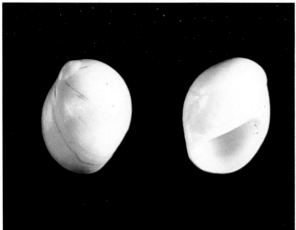

Polinices tumidus
(Swainson, 1840)

The Moon Shell. This species has long been known as *Polinices mamilla* but the exact identity of that species can not be established. *Polinices pyriformis* (Recluz) is a synonym, sometimes used for the more elongate form of this shell. In shape it varies in height, but is almost uniformly glossy white, with a thick callus closing the umbilicus. Operculum is thin and horny, closing the aperture. Shell up to 45 mm in height. Distribution general, very common.

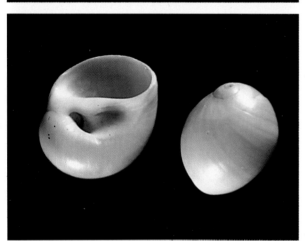

Neverita peselephanti
(Link, 1807)

Shell heavy and banded with brown broken by faint longitudinal paler lines. Umbilicus wide and deep, half covered by a thick columella callus. Operculum thin and horny, closing the aperture. Up to 50 mm. Distribution general, uncommon.

Neverita didyma
(Roeding, 1798)

The largest of the Moon Shells of this area, sometimes called the Shark's Eye. Grey-brown, glossy with striations running diagonally from the spire towards the base. Base white, umbilicus almost entirely closed by a brown sulcated umbilical callus. Interior of aperture brown. Early whorls encircled by a darker band giving the shell the appearance of a fish-like eye when viewed from above. Up to 70 mm. Operculum horny, closing the aperture. A favorite food for seagulls which drop the shells from a height onto rocks, breaking them open so that the bird can extract the soft parts with its beak (Seagulls do this with other species of mollusc as well). Distribution general. Common.

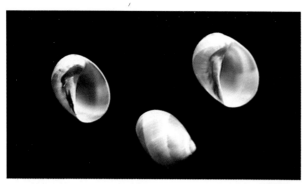

Mamilla melanostoma
(Gmelin, 1791)

A usually elongate brownish shell banded with darker brown round the very narrow umbilicus and a thick umbilical very dark brown callus. Aperture elongate, interior brownish, not capable of being completely closed by the horny operculum. Height up to 45 mm. Distribution general. Uncommon.

Sinum laevigatum
(Lamarck, 1822)

Ear-shaped shell, ivory white and not glossy, stained with brown inside the aperture. Virtually no spire at all. The animal completely envelops the shell and is unable to withdraw into it and close the aperture. Operculum thin, brown and corneous. Up to 40 mm. Distribution general. Uncommon.

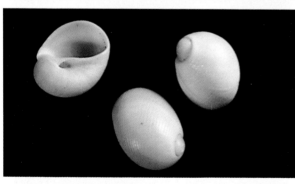

Eunaticina papilla
(Gmelin, 1791)

Shell somewhat similar in shape to *Mamilla sebae*, umbilicus wide and deep, columella straight, aperture very wide, horny brown operculum with a central nucleus, not closing the aperture. The shell is dull ivory with a thin yellowish periostracum and is coarsely spirally ridged. Up to 25 mm in height. The animal completely envelops the shell when moving. Distribution general, uncommon.

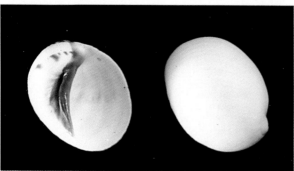

Mamilla sebae
(Recluz, 1844)

Similar in shape to *Mamilla melanostoma*, columella callus dark brown, likewise the umbilicus. Shell is not very glossy and is finely striate diagonally from the spire towards the base. Background color is white usually patterned in bands of brown longitudinal lines. Up to 45 mm. Interior of aperture white and glossy. Operculum thin and horny only partially closing the aperture. Distribution general. Uncommon.

Superfamily **Tonnacea**
Family **Cassididae (Bonnet Shells)**
Heavy, somewhat low-spired shells, with narrow apertures and usually an enlarged columella shield or callus. Carnivorous.

Semicassis faurotis
(Jousseaume, 1888)

Shell bluish-cream with reddish rectangular markings and a dark apex. The shell is more or less spirally ridged, smooth and shining, the columellar callus is extended and coarsely ridged at the bottom (anterior) and the outer lip is denticulate and ridged within. The operculum is strongly toothed or ridged, not fitting the aperture. The shell has the appearance of having two umbilici. Anterior canal sharply twisted back. Up to 60 mm. Distribution general. Uncommon. A similar shell, *Semicassis bisulcatum* (Schubert & Wagner, 1829), has been recorded from the Gulf of Oman but the dark apex instantly distinguishes between the two.

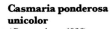

Casmaria ponderosa unicolor
(Dautzenberg, 1926)

Beautifully smooth, polished shells, greyish-green or cream and marked variously in brown. The last whorl is very bulbous especially towards the shoulder. Outer lip blotched with brown. Columella thick and twisted, anterior canal bent upwards and twisted. Up to 60 mm. Operculum small, yellow and fan-shaped. Distribution general. Usually found cast up, dead.

Phalium glaucum
(Linnaeus, 1758)

Juvenile shells are grooved, the adults are smooth and greyish. Up to 120 mm. The base of the outer lip has sharp pointed teeth. Interior of aperture brown, columellar shield orange, wrinkled. It has the appearance of having two umbilici. Operculum horny, brown, fan-shaped. Distribution general. Rare.

Family **Cymatiidae (Triton or Trumpet Shells)**

Mostly strong, heavy shells, usually with varices, no posterior canal, thickened outer lip, folded columella and toothed inner lip. Operculate, the operculum being thin and horny. Often the species have a hairy periostracum such as that of *Cymatium pileare*, the Hairy Triton. Most of this family are predatory carnivores, many eating starfish, or marine worms. Eggs are laid in capsules in rock crevices or on the underside of rocks.

The reason for the name "Trumpet Shell" is that the larger members of this group are used as horns or trumpets by cutting off the apex of the shell or drilling a hole in one of the upper whorls. Such horns are capable of making a loud sustained sound which reverberates through mountain passes, along beaches or over lakes. Some members of this family grow to a gigantic size, the famous Triton's Trumpet of the Indo-Pacific reaching lengths of 600 mm or more.

Cymatium moritinctum
Reeve, 1844

A heavy, squat shell with well rounded whorls, marked with brown bands on cream, darker at the varices. The ridges are finely striate longitudinally and the spaces between are finely ridged horizontally. The interior of the aperture is white, brown between the teeth within the outer lip and flushed with brown on the columella. Up to 65 mm. We have found this only at Salalah in Oman, though it is found elsewhere in the Indian Ocean. Rare.

Cymatium labiosum
(Wood, 1828)

A small, stout, heavy shell, cream marked with brown, with coarse, corded ridges and tuberculate ribs giving a cancellated appearance. Inner aperture and columella white. Up to 25 mm. Distribution general, uncommon. We have found it in shallow water in the intertidal zone, usually clinging to the underside of rocks.

Cymatium pileare
(Linnaeus, 1758)

An elongate, high spired shell, with strong varices and banded brown and cream. The periostracum is very fine and hairy, with hairs about one quarter of an inch in length. There are dark stains between the columella folds and between the paired white teeth inside the outer lip, which begin at the edge and extend deep into the pinkish lavender aperture. Up to 110 mm. To be found at low tide under stones. Distribution general, common.

Cymatium parthenopeum
(von Salis, 1793)

A solid shell with coarse ridges, tuberculated rather than varixed, with many shades of brown, white and black. Interior of aperture off-white, except for brown marking on the teeth of the inner lip and dark brown between the columella folds which are very close and numerous. Up to 130 mm. The specimens found at Masirah are usually larger than those from Muscat. We have found it in shallow water, under stones at the low tide level. Distribution general. Common.

Cymatium pileare aquatile
(Reeve, 1844)

Some authorities do not consider this to be a subspecies of the above, but a species, *Cymatium aquatile* Reeve in its own right. It differs from the above in having no brown markings between the columella folds, and in the teeth within the outer lip being short and discontinuous. The exterior is also lighter in color and more orange. Up to 110 mm. We have found it to a depth of about six feet at low tide, under rocks, and it is not difficult to find in the Muscat area. Common.

Cymatium trilineatum
Reeve, 1844

A strongly ridged shell, with fine ridges between the coarse ones, tuberculate where the varices cross the ridges. Spire has a turreted appearance, the upper whorls being cancellate. Light brown, marked with lighter color, interior of aperture and columella white. Up to 70 mm. Distribution general. Uncommon.

Cymatium tripus
(Lamarck, 1822)

A light brown, sturdy shell, small for the genus *Cymatium*. Siphonal canal long and slightly curved. Thick outer lip. The whorls have distinct nodules between the varices, which are crossed by strong spiral ribs. Aperture off-white, sometimes with a purplish tinge. Up to 55 mm. Usually found on sand. Distribution general. Rare.

Cymatium vespaceum
(Lamarck, 1822)

A small shell, ridged and tuberculate with one varix on the body whorl of adult specimens and a strong outer lip, finely toothed within. Pale brown or ivory indefinitely patterned with slightly darker brown. Interior of aperture lavender with a pale band in the center. Up to 35 mm. We have found it usually in sand between stones in shallow water in the intertidal zone. Distribution general. Common.

Linatella cingulata
(Lamarck, 1822)

A beautiful brown striped shell, horizontally ridged, without varices and with well rounded whorls, angled at the shoulders. Up to 60 mm. This species lives in shallow water, usually beneath stones. Distribution general. Rare.

Cymatium ranzanii
Bianconi, 1850

A large and beautiful member of the "Hairy Tritons", with strong varices and dark blotches on the columella and inner side of the outer lip. Up to 220 mm. The authors first discovered it in Oman in 1963 and since that time, a moderate number of specimens have been found. It is difficult to find as it lives where large waves are continually dashing against boulders and the currents are dangerous to divers, although it can be found in comparatively shallow water. Juveniles have a very thin and fragile lip, but young specimens are more attractive than the older ones which are often encrusted. The mantle is dotted black on white like a leopard. Distribution general. Rare.

Linatella clandestina
(Lamarck, 1822)

Similar to *Linatella cingulata*, but with rounded shoulders and a thickened, denticulate outer lip and longer anterior canal. Up to 60 mm. We have found it in the intertidal zone and to a depth of about six feet at low tide, clinging to the underside of rocks. Distribution general. Rare.

Ranularia boschi
Abbott and Lewis, 1970

A low-spired, heavy shell with turreted upper whorls and a strong varix on the body whorl. Anterior canal elongated and somewhat open. The ridges on the whorls are very tuberculate and the spaces between finely ridged. Outer lip very thickened with clumps of twin teeth within. Color pale, lightly marked with brown, with darker brown apex. Periostracum light brown and fairly thick. Up to 150 mm. We have found it primarily on a sandy substrate but have also found it clinging to the sides of rocks, in shallow water to a depth of about six feet. So far it is known only from Salalah and Masirah. The foot is dark grey and the operculum dark brown. Uncommon.

Ranularia oboesus
(Perry, 1811)

This shell has also been known as *Ranularia retusa* (Lamarck) which is a later synonym. It is a very flat spired shell with an unusually long siphonal canal, and a small aperture, with about five strong teeth within. Ivory in color marked with brown. Up to 60 mm. We have found it primarily under stones and rocks, moving about by means of a strong muscular foot. The operculum is dark brown. Distribution general. Rare.

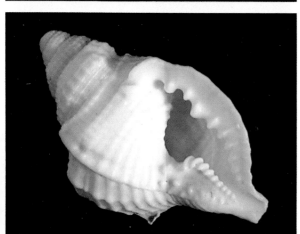

Distorsio reticulata
(Roeding, 1798)

A distorted, stumpy shell, cancellated in sculpture and with irregular, frilly varices and a flaring outer lip, strongly toothed. There is a pronounced notch in the columella, which is strongly plicate. Color cream, interior of aperture white. Up to 50 mm. We have found it among rocks in the low intertidal zone and only at Muscat where it is rare.

Family **Colubrariidae (False Tritons)**

Long narrow shells with varices, short anterior canal
and no posterior canal. Operculum horny.

Colubraria ceylonensis
(Sowerby, 1833)

An elongated shell with varices
on each whorl, ivory marked
with pale fawn or orange-brown,
aperture small and orange
within. Up to 55 mm. The
brown corneous operculum fills
the aperture. We have found it
on rocks in the low intertidal
zone, only at Masirah. Rare.

Family **Bursidae (Frog Shells)**

Similar to Cymatiidae but with a posterior canal or notch as well as anterior canal, and usually a toothed outer lip. Operculum thin but strong, horny. They have been called "Frog Shells" because of their warty, bumpy appearance, resembling a toad or frog. The majority live below low tide level and therefore are not usually obtained alive except by diving. Although most are found on sand, they are usually in the vicinity of rocks and some may be found clinging to the underside of rocks. The animals are carnivorous. The huge *Bursa bardeyi* makes a wonderful trumpet when the spire is cut off.

Bursa bardeyi
Jousseaume, 1894

The largest of the Frog Shells to be found in Oman, and one of its really fantastic shells; the largest specimens run up to 350 mm in length. These are obtained at Fahal Island, off Muscat, by diving, where we have usually found them resting on the bottom between two large rocks. Younger specimens have been found in shallow water, clinging to the sides of rocks. Each whorl has a row of large tubercules, the rest of the shell being ridged and slightly tuberculate. Usually brown in color with dashes of darker brown, older specimens being paler or even ivory. The interior of the aperture and the columella are white to orange, the interior of the outer lip having widely spaced, not very strong teeth, and the columella being very finely plicate. Distribution general, common.

Bursa bufonia
(Gmelin, 1791)

A very squat, heavy shell with coarse tubercules on the ridges and the posterior canal showing distinctly on each whorl, immediately above each other. Interior of aperture, outer lip and columella white or cream. Exterior of shell grey or cream marked sparsely with brown, often covered with lime or a chalky deposit. Up to 80 mm. Distribution general. Uncommon. The animals are carnivorous.

Bursa granularis
(Roeding, 1798)

Shell usually reddish-brown in color but sometimes a specimen is found which is almost red or even orange. Outer lip, columella and interior of aperture white. There are two rib-like varices on each whorl, the surface has spiral, finely beaded ridges. Up to 60 mm. Usually found under rocks at subtidal levels. Distribution general. Common.

Bursa rubeta
(Linnaeus, 1758)

Similar to *Bursa granularis* but with coarser sculpture and with the interior of the aperture red, and with a wider outer lip and columella. Up to 85 mm. Distribution general. Uncommon.

Bursa spinosa
(Lamarck, 1816)

A pale, moderately light-weight shell, characterized by the spines protruding from the varices. In some specimens these spines are more prominent than those shown in the accompanying illustration. Up to 60 mm. Distribution general, uncommon.

Family **Tonnidae (Tun Shells)**

Characterized by their large rounded shape, low spires and thin shells. No operculum. Most specimens live in deep water and hence they are rarely found in good condition; one usually finds them on the beaches occupied by hermit crabs. The animals are carnivorous and prey upon sea urchins, molluscs and other marine animals. The salivary glands secrete a substance which renders the victim powerless; it is an acid-containing substance which is thought to be a neuro-toxin. Once paralysed, the Tonna can ingest the prey at will. This is a difficult family to identify as the juveniles vary considerably from the adults and the sculpture amongst species varies from specimen to specimen, as does the color.

Tonna cumingii
(Reeve, 1849)

Very similar to *Tonna cepa* (Roeding) and considered to be a variety of this by some authors, but always to be distinguished by the "dints" or tiny indentations in the surface of the shell. Broad ridges encircle the surface which is variously patterned in brown and cream, usually with a somewhat cloudy or marbled effect. Up to 70 mm. Occasionally we have found this species in deep intertidal pools, but it usually lives in deeper water. Distribution general. Uncommon.

Tonna dolium
(Linnaeus, 1758)

An extremely variable species indeed, the whorls being encircled with ridges of varying size and width, interspaced by smaller ridges and fine grooves. Young specimens have more evenly rounded ridges with less grooving between and are often spotted with orange-red (these have been called *Tonna tessellata* (Lamarck)). Some of the very old specimens are plain dirty white or cream. Up to 150 mm. Distribution general. Common.

Tonna luteostoma
(Kuester, 1857)

A heavier and more regular shell than the preceding species, with rounded spiral ridges fairly evenly spaced, with a small ridge between the upper wide ridges. Mottled brown on cream and fairly glossy. Up to 170 mm. Distribution general. Fairly common.

Family **Ficidae (Fig Shells)**

The name "Ficus" comes from the Latin word meaning "Fig". Elegantly curved, light, thin shells, with low spires, long anterior canals and wide apertures. No operculum. The foot is large and the shell partly covered by the mantle of the live animal as it glides about on the sand. Carnivorous. The shape of these shells makes them useful as feeding utensils. We have seen mothers giving milk to their babies by using a fig shell, which, it seemed to us, was a better feeding instrument than a spoon. There are two species of this family in Oman, but one has not yet been identified to our satisfaction.

Ficus subintermedia
(d'Orbigny, 1852)

Very flat-spired, with reticulate sculpture. The ground color is light pinkish-brown, flecked with brown and the interior of the aperture is a mauvish-brown. Up to 75 mm. We have found it in sandy areas in the shallow sub-tidal zone. Distribution general. Common. The other species is not reticulate in sculpture and is rare.

Order **Neogastropoda**

Superfamily **Muricacea**
Family **Muricidae**

Exceedingly varied in shape and ornament, most
members of this family have elaborate and sometimes
intricate spines or fronds or varices. Murexes are
famous for the degree of "hunter instinct" they display.
All are voracious predators, drilling holes in other
molluscs or forcing open the shells so as to devour the
animal within. The animals have a gland which
produces special enzymes for softening the victim's shell
and a boring organ associated with the radula for
drilling into their victims. Historically Murex shells
were famous because of the Tyrian purple dye from
Tyre and Sidon which was obtained by crushing the
shells to obtain the slimy clear fluid which produced
this enduring color. So prestigious were the purple
garments that even today purple is a royal color. All
Murex shells have a horny operculum which is sturdy
and strong.

Murex haustellum
Linnaeus, 1758

The "Snipe's Bill Murex".
Rounded whorls, with three
varices per whorl, color brown
patterned with darker brown,
anterior canal very long and
almost closed, interior of
aperture and columella pink. Up
to 150mm. Distribution general.
Rare.

Chicoreus ramosus
(Linnaeus, 1758)

One of the largest species of Murex in Oman, up to 250 mm. A striking shell with elaborate frilly fronds growing from the varices, cream in color with the interior of the aperture pink. In Oman this species is uncommon, except at Fahal Island where it can be found quite easily.

Murex malabaricus
Smith, 1894

A brown colored thick shell with a large body whorl and an unusually long siphonal canal. In some specimens the siphonal canal makes up to 50% of the shell's length. There are three strong axial varices which carry small spines. The body whorl has six axial ribs between each of the varices, and there are numerous spiral ridges on the whorls and varices. Aperture white, almost round, completely closed by the dark brown operculum. The basic off-white color is banded with light to dark brown lines. Up to 120 mm. This species is a sand-dweller and carnivorous. We have dredged several specimens in about 50 feet of water off Muscat, but have not found it anywhere else. Rare.

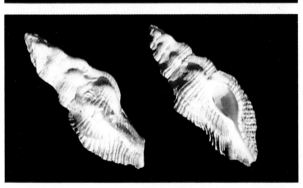

Pterynotus albobrunneus
d'Attilio & Bertsch, 1980

An elongated shell with a tall spire and flattened winglike fronds or varices. It differs from *Pterynotus pellucidus* (Reeve) in having narrower, coarser varices and in being tinged with greyish brown, instead of being pure white. This shell is mentioned by Emily Vokes (1978, "Muricidae from the eastern coast of Africa" published in the Annals of the National Museum) who had seen only one shell from Mozambique. The only other recorded specimen, the holotype, was dredged in deep water off Kil'an I., Laccadives in 1978. So far we have found several specimens at various localities along the coast of Oman. Up to 60 mm. Rare.

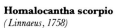

Homalocantha scorpio
(Linnaeus, 1758)

This shell has an astonishing array of brown fronds and spines. Smaller spines are interspersed between larger ones and the tips of the spines are bifurcated. The spire is long and gives the impression of being out of alignment with the remainder of the shell. Up to 60 mm. We have found it only in a dead state along the beaches. Rare.

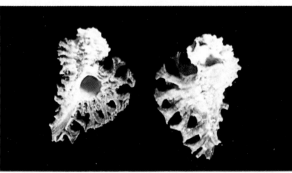

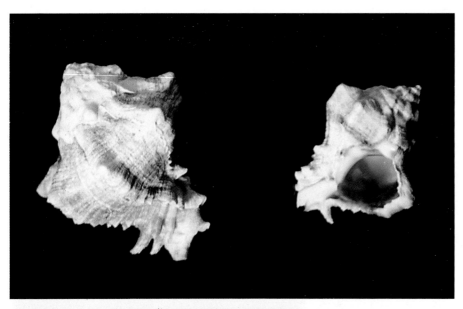

Hexaplex kuesterianus
(Tapparone-Canefri, 1875)

Young specimens of this shell have fairly elaborate short frilly spines growing from the varices, but as the shell becomes older the spines wear down and the adult is a very thick heavy squat looking shell. Due to this variation in appearance this shell has several synonyms, among them being *Murex spinosus* and *Murex turbinatus*. It has also been confused with the Red Sea *Murex anguliferus* from which it differs most noticeably in having a double row of spikes round the anterior canal and in the anterior canal being shorter and broader. Up to 120 mm. We have found it in rocky areas, in sand or under rocks. Distribution general. Common.

Murex scolopax
Dillwyn, 1817

A cream to grey globose shell with a long anterior canal and long spines protruding from the varices. There are weak spiral ridges running round the whorls. Up to 180 mm. This is the only spiny murex that has been recorded from Oman but two other similar species have been recorded from other parts of the Gulf; collectors should be on the lookout for the possibility that these others may also occur in Oman. This species lives in silty muddy areas and is a shallow water species; we have not found it below a depth of about five feet at low tide. When walking over the habitat of this shell, which is usually well camouflaged by weed attached to the spines, it is easy to get one of the spines deeply embedded into one's foot. Such a broken spine shows up well on X-Ray, but can be very difficult to remove. For this reason (and others) it is always wise to wear protective footwear when walking the beaches at low tide. Distribution general. Common but rarely found without some broken spines. We have observed these animals drilling into other molluscs in our aquarium.

Family **Thaididae (Dog Whelks or Rock Shells)**
In general these shells are solid and heavy for their size, which is mostly small. Most have a relatively large aperture and crenulated outer lip. Many have strong rounded ribs or spines which give them a bumpy, nodular look. The operculum is corneous, usually dark brown and thin. The animals are carnivorous, often eating barnacles and thin shelled bivalves. They are primarily a shallow water family, many living in the intertidal zone, and nearly always associated with rocks, hence the name "Rock Shells".

Thais bufo
(Lamarck, 1822)

A low-spired, very rounded shell, weakly ridged and slightly tuberculate, with an exceptionally large aperture giving one the feeling that this species is "all mouth". Exterior is dull brown or greyish and the interior of the aperture and the columella are cream to yellowish. Up to 70 mm. We have found it on the sides of rocks, and not underneath them. Distribution general. Relatively common. Some authorities call this shell *Mancinella bufo*.

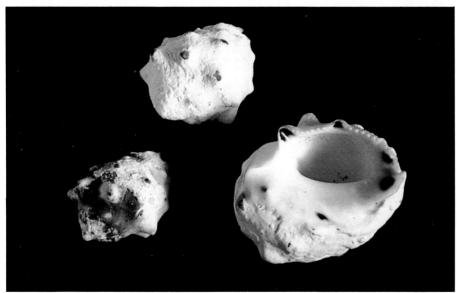

Thais bimaculatus
(Jonas, 1845)

The most striking feature of this shell is its "whiteness" punctuated by rows of black tubercules and the conspicuous, circular black blotches at the base of the white columella and outer lip. Up to 55 mm. We have usually found it on the shore side of rocks, apparently preferring the shelter of the rock rather than exposure to the force of the waves. The foot of the animal is dark, almost black and the operculum is dark brown. We have observed *Thais bimaculatus* devouring a limpet. Distribution general. Uncommon.

Thais mancinella
(Linnaeus, 1758)

A heavy, brownish shell, finely ridged and with rows of spiky tubercules. The interior of the aperture is orange and ridged, the columella orange. Up to 75 mm. We have often found this species in exposed positions on the tops or sides of rocks, where it is at the mercy of large waves. The foot of the animal is dark grey. Distribution general, common, particularly around Muscat and Muttrah.

Thais mutabilis
(Link, 1807)

A synonym is *Thais carinifera* (Lamarck) by which name it is possibly better known. In young shells the spire is noticeably turreted and coronate, with sharp, upcurving spikes. The shoulder of the body whorl is also coronate. The rest of the body whorl is ridged with fine striae between the ridges. Exterior is cream to fawn, sometimes marked with brown. The interior of the aperture and the columella are pinkish cream. Older shells become coarse and not so delicate and the coronations are not so pronounced. Up to 80 mm. The foot of the animal is dark grey. We have observed *Thais mutabilis* devouring a small *Cardium pseudolima*. Distribution general. Relatively uncommon, except at Mahawt, off the southern coast of Oman, where it is common.

Thais rugosa
(Born, 1778)

In some ways this species resembles *Thais mutabilis*, but the spire is higher, the color is dark brown and there is a fine ridge between the coarse tuberculate ridges which encircle the body whorl. Columella and interior of the aperture are white. Up to 50 mm. We have found it only at Masirah. Rare.

Thais savignyi
Deshayes, 1844

A very strongly ridged shell, the ridges being with large tubercules, brown on a dull grey background, Columella and interior of aperture white, the outer lip having a black rim. Up to 60 mm. The foot of the animal is dark and we usually find it in exposed positions. Distribution general. Very common. This shell has been called *Thais pseudohippocastanum* Dautzenberg which is a synonym.

Thais tissoti
(Petit, 1853)

A small shell, very strongly ridged and slightly tuberculate, high-spired and with a particularly well developed shoulder. Interior of the aperture is cream colored and often has brown bands running spirally within. Columella white, flushed with cream or mushroom. Exterior of the shell is pale lined with brown. Up to 35 mm. Distribution general. Common.

Nassa francolina
(Bruguière, 1789)

An elongated, very smooth shell with a long and wide aperture, edged with brown on the outer lip and pinkish within. Columella dark brown flushed with pink. The exterior of the shell is very finely striate, dark brown in color with an irregular band of light mauvish blotches around the widest part of the body whorl. Up to 70 mm. This seems to be a shallow water species; we have found it living under stones, coral or rubble in the intertidal zone. Distribution general. Uncommon.

Vexilla vexillum
(Gmelin, 1791)

A small smooth oval shell, striped with light and dark brown. There is a tooth at the top of the columella. Interior of aperture white. Up to 30 mm. We have found this species in sand, which is unusual for this family, but always near rocks and sometimes on or under them. We have found it from the low tide level to a depth of about six feet. Distribution general. Uncommon.

Purpura rudolphi
Lamarck, 1822

A dark brown, almost black shell with coarse spiral ridges interspaced with several fine ridges. The coarse ridges have tubercules and are marked with dashes of black and white. Aperture is white within, bordered by pink and edged with brown on the outer lip. Columella is pink. Up to 80 mm. The foot of the animal is dark grey. We have often found it in tide pools between rocks and in other sheltered places. Distribution general. Common. A very similar shell, *Purpura persica* (Linnaeus, 1758) has also been recorded from the Gulf of Oman. It lacks the tubercules on the ridges.

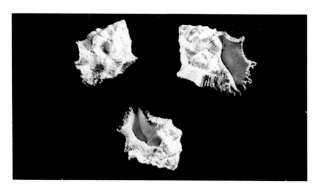

Morula chrysostoma
(Deshayes, 1844)

A small shell, very heavily built for its size, with sharp spiky tubercules. The exterior is finely striated between the rows of tubercules and is brown, often covered by a chalky deposit. Up to 35 mm. There are strong denticles within the outer lip and the aperture is a beautiful orange. The foot of the animal is dark brown. We have found it on rocks or in crevices. Distribution general. Very common.

Rapana bulbosa
(Solander, 1817)

This shell has been called *Rapana rapiformis* (Born) but it is not certain for which of two species Born intended this name. The shell is light in weight and globose with a low, pointed spire, up to 102 mm. The exterior is finely striate with slightly tuberculate ridges and a row of sharp pointed tubercules at the shoulder, pale brown in color. The umbilicus is very open and deep, the aperture very wide, ridged inside and pale pink to deep salmon in color. The foot of the animal is dark grey. We have found it in shallow water at low tide. Distribution general. Relatively uncommon.

Cronia konkanensis
(Melvill, 1893)

An elongated shell, the height of the spire equalling that of the aperture, black nodules on a paler background and with moderately strong horizontal ridges across and between the tubercules. Up to 30 mm. Inner edge of the outer lip is black and white, the interior, columella and denticles bluish white. It lives in rocky areas, exposed to the pounding of waves and can easily be collected in the intertidal zone. Distribution general. Very common.

Morula granulata
(Duclos, 1832)

A "warty" little black and white shell, up to 27 mm. The inner edge of the outer lip is black, with a few small sharp white denticles. The interior is bluish white, the columella the same, touched with dark brown at the anterior and posterior ends. Although the color of the shell serves as an excellent camouflage, this species can easily be found at low tides, on stones and rocks. Distribution general. Very common.

Family **Coralliophilidae (Coral Shells)**
This family lives in or among coral. The shells are often
covered with coralline or lime deposits. They have a
wide aperture, a thin, brown horny operculum and no
radula, the mouth and digestive system being especially
adapted for feeding on the coral polyps.

Coralliophila gyrata
(Hinds, 1844)

An elongated white shell with
turreted whorls and flat
shoulders. It is finely ridged and
has a long anterior canal, and a
deep narrow umbilicus. Up to 65
mm. It is sometimes called
Latiaxis gyratus, as there is some
difference of opinion among
scientists as to the exact status of
the various species in this family.
Distribution general. Rare.

Coralliophila erosa
(Roeding 1798)

An irregularly shaped shell,
ridged and with weak
longitudinal ridges, pale brown
in color, up to 40 mm. Aperture
is ridged and deep purple, the
outer lip edged with white.
Distribution general. Rare.

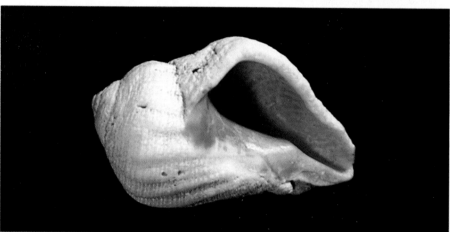

Coralliophila neritoidea
(Lamarck, 1822)

A globose shell with fine
horizontal ridges and a spire
which can be short or high. It
has a broad violet columella and
the interior of the aperture is
violet, the outer lip strongly
toothed. Up to 50 mm. We have
found this species only at
Masirah. Rare.

Coralliophila costularis
(Lamarck, 1816)

Similar to *Coralliophila erosa*
but much more elongated and
with a high spire. Up to 40 mm.
We have found this species only
at Masirah. Rare.

Superfamily **Buccinacea**
Family **Columbellidae (Dove Shells)**
Shells usually small, with pointed apices and narrow apertures. No posterior canal. Outer lip usually thickened in the center and toothed. Horny thin operculum.

Pyrene testudinaria
(Link, 1807)

Small, multi-colored sometimes spotted, smooth shells, up to 25 mm, with rounded whorls and a thickened outer lip. We have found this species in shallow water in the intertidal zone, always on rocks or in tide pools, only at Salalah and Masirah. It is very common at Salalah.

Mitrella blanda
(Sowerby, 1844)

Elongate smooth small shells with narrow apertures and deep sutures between the whorls. Up to 18 mm. The shell is patterned with attractive zigzag markings of brown on white and often there is a greyish smudge near the shoulder on the back of the last whorl. We have found it to date only at Muscat and Masirah. Uncommon.

Anachis misera
(Sowerby, 1844)

Small longitudinally ribbed shells, the ribs being dark brown or black with brown or ivory between them and usually with a white line at the top of the shoulder below the suture. Up to 16 mm. *Anachis zebra* (Gray) is a synonym. We have found it on and under rocks in the intertidal zone. Distribution general. Very common.

Family **Buccinidae (Whelks)**

Shells sometimes spindle-shaped and sometimes globular, operculum thin and horny. Most species are predators or carrion feeders. The carnivorous species do not bore holes into the shells of other molluscs but attack accessible parts or force open the valves of bivalves by inserting part of their own shell.

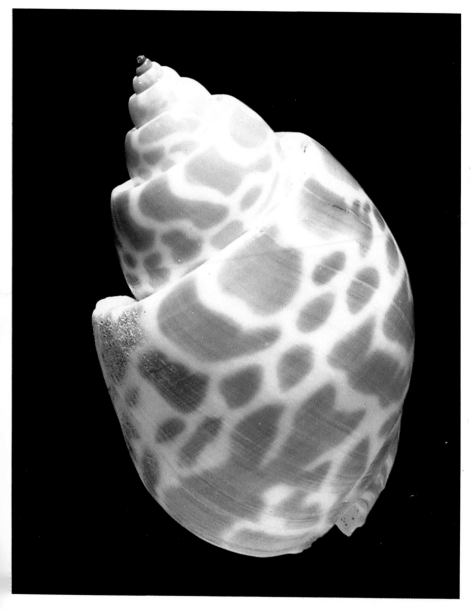

Babylonia spirata
(Linnaeus, 1758)

The name fits the shell perfectly, as it looks very much like the spiral towers of Babylon with its sharp shoulders, deep suture and turreted spire. It has a deep umbilicus and is a strong, colorful shell, patterned red-brown on white. Up to 75 mm. This species lives in sandy areas among rocks, moving about by means of a strong, muscular foot. Distribution general. Common. Dead shells, occupied by hermit crabs, are easy to find on all beaches.

Engina mendicaria
(Linnaeus, 1758)

A small heavy shell, black and yellow spiral bands on the whorls. Sometimes the bands are nearly white. Interior of aperture dark, outer lip toothed. Up to 20 mm. It can be found by turning over rocks and stones at the low tide level, or in rocky crevices. Distribution general. Common.

Cantharus undosus
(Linnaeus, 1758)

Shell with brown spiral ridges on a paler background and rounded whorls, sometimes with very weak longitudinal ribs. Aperture pale within. Up to 35 mm. We have usually found it in sand in shallow water, sometimes on or near rocks. Distribution general. Common.

Hindsia bitubercularis
A. Adams, 1851

Hindsia suturalis A. Adams is a synonym. A high-spired shell with marked shoulders and strongly ribbed, rounded whorls. The ribs are crossed by fine spiral ridges. The ribs cause indentations within the aperture of the shell. The color is mostly white, sometimes lightly marked with brown. Up to 30 mm. We have found this species only at Masirah. Rare.

Cantharus spiralis
(Gray, 1846)

A heavy, thick shell with marked shoulders and strong spiral ridges. Brown in color with the interior of the aperture white and the outer lip fluted. There are fine striae crossing the ridges. Up to 45 mm. This species is a scavenger and often attacks other molluscs as well. We have found it in the intertidal zone beneath rocks; at low tides as many as ten specimens may be found beneath a single stone. Distribution Salalah and Masirah, where it is common.

Pisania rubiginosa
(Reeve, 1846)

In shape similar to *Pisania ignea*, but plain reddish-brown in color with fine, rather curved, longitudinal ribs crossing very fine spiral ridges, so that the shell has a cancellated appearance. Up to 40 mm. To date, we have found this only at Masirah on rocks in the low intertidal zone. Rare.

Pisania ignea
(Gmelin, 1791)

An elongated, somewhat spindle-shaped shell, the aperture being half the height of the shell. Up to 50 mm. The color is variable but browns and reddish-browns predominate. We have usually found these on rocks in the low intertidal zone. Distribution general. Fairly common.

Family **Melongenidae**

Shells with a short spire, large body whorl, long anterior canal and thick horny operculum. Carnivorous or carrion feeders.

Taphon striatum
(Sowerby, 1833)

Light-weight shell, with a low spire, very rounded body-whorl and long slightly curved anterior canal. Up to 80 mm. The sutures are deep. The interior of the aperture is finely ridged and white. There are two color forms of this species, one having brown and white fine spiral lines and the other being paler, and only sparsely blotched or lined with brown. The operculum is thick and brown. We have found it in shallow water, frequently near rocks. Distribution Salalah and Masirah only. Rare.

Family **Nassariidae**
(Dog Whelks or Basket Whelks)

Shells with anterior canal and posterior notch.
Aperture usually roundish and often with a columella
callus. Operculum thin and horny, often with serrated
edges. Carrion feeders or predatory gastropods, preying
on marine animals and molluscs.

Bullia mauritiana
Gray, 1839

An elongated shell with deep
sutures, keeled shoulders and a
large body whorl with a wide,
flaring aperture, brown within.
Up to 75 mm. The exterior color
is variable, usually grey, or
cream. The animal has a very
large, powerful white foot, which
it charges with water to give it
strength. It lives in sandy flats
and beaches. Distribution
general. Common.

Bullia semiplicata
Gray, 1839

Distinguished from *Bullia
mauritiana* by the plicate or
ribbed appearance of the upper
parts of the whorls. Up to 35
mm. Interior of aperture pale.
Distribution general. Rare.

Bullia tranquebarica
(Roeding, 1798)

Bullia belangeri and *Bullia lineolata* are synonyms of this. The shell is spirally ridged with flat ridges separated by fine grooves, with deeper grooves just below the suture and at the base of the body whorl. Aperture cream to brown within, columella white. Externally grey-brown to pale brown in color. Up to 45 mm. Distribution general. Common.

Bullia rogersi
Smythe 1981

This is similar in shape to *Bullia tranquebarica* but the surface is smooth and glossy. The suture is deep and the ivory surface is marked by longitudinal brown streaks and brown dots at the shoulders. This is a new species, which has been named by Kathleen Smythe. Up to 28 mm. Distribution Masirah only. Uncommon.

Bullia tahitensis
(Gmelin, 1791)

Similar in shape to *Bullia tranquebarica* but strongly spirally ridged with rounded ridges. Whorls very rounded and there is a deep groove round the base of the body whorl. Aperture pinkish within, with a pale edge to the lip. External color is creamy-grey. Up to 55 mm. We have found this only at Salalah and Masirah. Rare.

Nassarius gaudiosus
(Hinds, 1844)

A smooth, glossy attractively patterned shell with rounded whorls, the upper ones being slightly ribbed. Columellar callus is not very expanded and somewhat transparent. The outer lip has a few short denticles which extend a little way into the purplish banded interior of the aperture. Up to 30 mm. There are several synonyms one of which is *Nassarius pictus* (Dunker). We have found it only at Masirah where it is very common.

Nassarius arcularius plicatus
(Roeding, 1798)

This species has often been mistakenly called *Nassarius pullus* which does not occur in the Indian Ocean. It has coarse slanting ribs which are crossed to a greater or lesser degree by fine spiral striae and the shoulders are tuberculate. The white columella callus spreads largely over the body whorl. The aperture is brownish or brown-banded within and is ridged. Externally the color is cream to grey or brown. Up to 28 mm. These shells are active scavengers and we have observed several hundreds of them feeding on a single dead fish. Distribution general. Very common.

Nassarius albescens gemmuliferus
(A. Adams, 1852)

Shell is sculptured with beaded slanting longitudinal ribs, sometimes with fine spiral ridges between the rows of beads. The columella callus is white, thick and porcelaneous, squarish in shape and extending onto the body whorl. The interior of the aperture is usually banded with brown and is ridged, aperture is narrow and the short anterior canal and posterior notch are moderately narrow. The exterior color is cream to pale brown or grey. Up to 20 mm. Distribution general. Common.

Nassarius coronatus
(Bruguière, 1789)

This shell is large for the Nassarius group of species, up to 50 mm. It is usually a creamy or pinkish color, sometimes slightly banded spirally. It has tubercules on the shoulders and a few ribs just behind the edge of the outer lip. The columellar callus is not very expanded. Adults have several sharp points on the outer anterior edge of the lip. Interior of the aperture is usually darker. Distribution general. Common.

Nassarius glans
(Linnaeus, 1758)

Similar in shape to *Nassarius gaudiosus* but with a smooth cream interior to the aperture. The color is light with occasional brown flashes and lined spirally with brown or reddish brown, making it one of the more attractive of the "Dog Whelks" Up to 50 mm. Distribution general. Rare.

Nassarius nodiferus
(Powys, 1835)

The shell has coarse slanting ribs which are constricted by a groove below the suture and crossed by spiral ridges on the anterior part of the body whorl. The columella callus is moderately wide, the outer lip ridged within and the interior of the aperture dark purple brown. Up to 32 mm. We have found this species in sand at low tide levels. Distribution general. Uncommon.

Nassarius deshayesiana
Issel, 1865

A small species of Nassarius with strong longitudinal ribs, widely separated, crossed by fine spiral ridges which give the ribs a beaded appearance. The color is cream patterned with grey or brown. The columella callus is yellow, and tuberculate at the anterior in adult specimens; it does not cover the body whorl. The outer lip is finely toothed within and the interior of the aperture is banded with brown. Up to 15 mm. Distribution general on rocks and in sand. Very common.

Family **Fasciolariidae (Tulip or Spindle Shells)**

Spindle shaped shells, usually high-spired and with long, sometimes twisted or curved anterior canals, operculum horny with a terminal nucleus. Carnivorous.

In Oman, the women use the operculum of *Fasciolaria trapezium* and *Chicoreus ramosus* to make a form of incense. The operculum is ground up until it becomes a powder, after which sugar and local spices are added until it resembles large chunks of brown sugar. The completed preparation is placed in an incense burner, the delicate aroma providing a special treat for visitors.

Fasciolaria trapezium
(Linnaeus, 1758)

A solid heavy shell, tuberculate at the shoulders, brown in color with lines of darker brown spirally, and also in the interior of the lighter-colored aperture. The periostracum is dark. This shell grows to be almost a foot long (280 mm) in the waters around Muscat, where the largest specimens are to be found at Fahal Island about two miles off the coast. The operculum is very thick, corneous and strong. We have found it at depths of between three and fifteen feet below the surface at low tide, moving about on the sand, but always near rocks. Distribution is general. Common.

The mature shell is extremely heavy and makes an excellent trumpet when the tip of the spire is cut off.

Peristernia rhodostoma
(A. Adams, 1885)

A spirally ridged shell, banded brown and white and with rounded ribs and a deep umbilicus. The anterior canal is narrow and purple within, as is the interior of the aperture and the columella. Up to 40 mm. The operculum is brown and horny. We have found it in shallow water near coral reefs, only at Masirah. Rare.

Fasciolaria trapezium audouini
(Jonas, 1846)

A smaller, lighter form lacking the heavy shoulder tubercules, which occurs in the south of Oman. Up to 150 mm.

Latirus species

A beautiful brown colored shell with distinct nodules and fine white stripes. There are spiral ridges with finer ridges between and coarse white ridges on the siphonal canal. The columella and the interior of the aperture is brown. Up to 70 mm. It lives in shallow water in the sandy areas between rocks. We have found it only at Masirah. Rare.

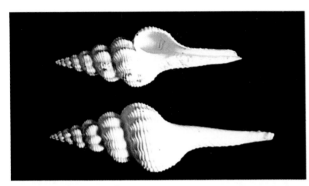

Fusinus forceps
(Perry, 1811)

This species has well rounded whorls, rounded ribs and coarse spiral ridges. The suture is deeply indented. The long siphonal canal is about five-eighths the length of the shell, which is entirely white. Up to 145 mm. We have found it only at Masirah. Rare.

Fusinus arabicus
(Melvill, 1898)

This species has a very long, narrow siphonal canal and a long spire. The whorls are rounded and spirally ridged with a cord-like ridge just below the suture. It is usually pale brown with cream ridges where they cross the weak longitudinal ribs. Up to 130 mm, but usually smaller. The operculum is thin. It lives in sand and can be found at low tide levels all along the Batinah Coast beaches. Distribution general. Common.

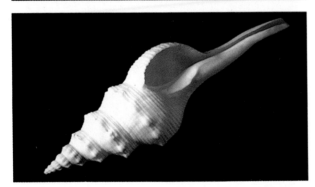

Fusinus townsendi
(Melvill, 1899)

Very similar to *Fusinus arabicus* but the whorls are keeled or angular instead of being rounded with sharp points on the ribs at the keel. The suture is deep. Most specimens are pale ivory tinged with brown, but we have found pure white ones. The average size of this shell is about 70 mm but we have found some gigantic pure white ones up to 220 mm. It lives on a sandy substrate and we have found it only at Masirah. Rare.

Peristernia nassatula forskalii
(Tapparone Canefri, 1875)

Some authorities consider that this is a species in its own right and not a subspecies. Cream, banded with brown, sometimes almost brown all over, with rounded ribs and coarse spiral ridges. The whorls are rounded, the siphonal canal fairly wide open and the interior of the narrow aperture deep purple or violet. Up to 35 mm. This species lives on the underside of rocks. We have never found it deeper than two or three feet at low tide. The operculum is relatively thick for the size of the shell. Distribution general. Common.

Superfamily **Volutacea**
Family **Olividae**

Cylindrical, short-spired glossy shells with long, narrow apertures, and folded or plicate columella. With or without operculum. Carnivorous animals which feed on small crabs or other invertebrates, folding their prey within their large foot and smothering it.

Oliva bulbosa
(Roeding, 1798)

The glossy outer layer of the shell is produced by special cells in the mantle. It is found in a wide variety of patterns, rarely entirely orange or dark grey or black. Most have checked markings reminiscent of Indian teepees. The base of the columella and interior of aperture are usually white. Older shells become very heavy and swollen with the upper edge of the columella or inner lip projecting strongly above the apex and the outer lip much thickened. Young shells are slim but can be distinguished from *Oliva oliva* (Linnaeus) by the deeper suture and incipient projection of the inner lip towards the apex. Also the columella has one very coarse plication above several weaker ones. Up to 65 mm, those at Masirah usually being larger than those near Muscat. Distribution general in sand. Very common. At low tide, *Oliva bulbosa* can be found plowing its way along leaving a tell-tale track behind it.

Ancilla castenea
(Sowerby, 1830)

In *Ancilla* the aperture is wider at the anterior than in *Oliva*. The shell of this species is usually a bright chocolate-brown, the color being uniform and consistent. However, it can vary from golden-brown to white. The short columella is white. Some specimens have faint stripes running down the shell. In Oman, the dark forms predominate. Up to 48 mm. Distribution general in sand. Common.

Ancilla species

There is another species of
Ancilla found in Oman, which is
brownish, spirally banded with
white and has a thin corneous
operculum. It is a new species,
currently under study, and will
be named soon. We have found
it only at Masirah where it is
locally common.

Ancilla ovalis
(Sowerby, 1830)

A small *Ancilla*, well rounded
with a light shell, variously
patterned in brown usually in
spiral bands. The base of the
columella is often tinged with
brown. Up to 17 mm. It lives in
sand or muddy flats and moves
about at night, usually just
below the surface. Distribution
general. Rare.

Ancilla ampla
(Gmelin, 1791)

A small white, solid, heavy,
glossy shell with a conical spire
and a long, wide aperture three-
quarters the length of the shell.
Up to 15 mm. Distribution
general. Rare.

Ancilla scaphella
(Sowerby, 1830)

The shell is slender, white and
light in weight; sometimes
specimens are found which show
a tinge of yellow or orange. It is
easily distinguished from all
other members of this family by
the fragile and comparatively
less glossy shell. It lives in sand
and is frequently washed up on
the Batinah coast. Up to 38 mm.
Distribution general. Common.

Family **Mitridae**

Usually long-spired shells with long, narrow apertures, sometimes half the length of the shell, and folded columellas. No operculum. Some species have a thin periostracum. The habitats of the species vary widely. Some live in sand, others under rocks or seaweed, and others on or under coral. Some species, when disturbed, emit a foul-smelling purplish liquid which is probably injurious to other marine creatures but is not harmful to humans. They are carnivorous, and scavengers.

Mitra guttata
Swainson, 1844

A light brown, glossy, smooth shell with an aperture more than half the length of the shell; there are fine spiral grooves on the rounded whorls and the suture is noticeably irregular, somewhat wavy rather than being clear cut and straight. Up to 60 mm. We have found this species washed up on the beaches at Masirah where it is rare. It is believed that no live specimens have ever been found.

Mitra pretiosa
Reeve, 1844

A very pretty Mitre with clearly indented sutures, white with brown markings on the spiral, rather beaded ridges – it has a slightly cancellated appearance due to the weak longitudinal striae which cross the ridges. The columella and the interior of the aperture are cream. The aperture is more than half the length of the shell. Up to 50 mm. We have found this only at Masirah where it is rare.

Mitra mitra
(Linnaeus, 1758)

This is the largest of the Mitres found in Oman, attaining a length of 180 mm. It is a strong, tapered shell, with an aperture almost half the length of the shell. It is conspicuously patterned with red-brown squarish marks in spiral rows across the whorls and the columella and interior of the aperture are ivory. It lives in shallow water in sandy areas. We have found it only at Masirah, and on isolated beaches ten miles south of Qurayat. Uncommon.

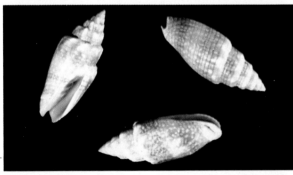

Mitra bovei
Kiener, 1838

A very sturdy shell, with deep sutures and strongly angled shoulders to each whorl. Wavy spiral grooves on the shell which is usually ivory in color, ornamented variably with greenish-brown spots and bands, and the interior of the aperture greenish or purple. Aperture is half the length of the shell. Up to 55 mm. Distribution general. Rare.

Mitra aurantia subruppeli
Finlay, 1927

A pale brown or fawn shell, ovate, with the aperture about half the length of the shell. It has strong spiral cord-like ridges and the columella and interior of the aperture are white. Up to 35 mm. We have found it in shallow water on sand, usually near to stones, or rocks at the low tide level. Distribution general but more common at Masirah. Rare.

Mitra punctostriata
A. Adams, 1855

A small brown shell, rather long in proportion to its width with rounded whorls which have spiral punctate grooves and deep sutures. The columella and interior of the aperture are cream. Up to 40 mm. We have found this only at Masirah where it is rare.

Mitra sanguinolenta
Lamarck, 1811

The shell is reddish in color, hence its name "sanguinolenta" taken from the Latin word "sanguinari" meaning blood-red. It is patterned with lines of deeper red or orange-red. Columella and aperture are cream. Up to 30 mm. We have found it only at Masirah. Rare.

Mitra (Strigatella) litterata
Lamarck, 1811

This is the commonest of the Mitres living in Oman. A heavy, solid, well-rounded little shell with a thickened outer lip and a thin brownish periostracum. The patterns are extremely variable: the shell is usually cream ornamented with wavy lines and blotches of brown or dark green, the columella and aperture being ivory to purple. The shell has spiral rows of small punctuations. Up to 30 mm. Found on sand near rocks or on the rocks themselves at the low tide level. Distribution general.

Mitra (Strigatella) scutulata
(Gmelin, 1791)

A synonym is *Mitra nebrias* Melvill. A smooth, glossy dark brown shell, sometimes slightly patterned with longitudinal dashes or stripes of a paler color. It has a pointed apex and the aperture, which is whitish inside, is about two-thirds the length of the shell. There are very fine spiral grooves on the whorls. Up to 35 mm. We have found it only at Masirah. Rare.

Pusia osiridis
(Issel, 1869)

An ivory or white shell banded with brown, the brown of the upper whorls only showing as spiral lines above the suture. The shoulders are angled and strongly tuberculate. The columella has four teeth, the posterior one being the most prominent. The interior of the aperture is finely striate. There are two spiral beaded rows on the anterior of the body whorl. Up to 42 mm. We have found it only at Masirah. Rare.

Cancilla isabella
Swainson, 1840

A long, tapered shell with an aperture almost half the length of the shell. The surface has a finely cancellated appearance and is pale brown with a lighter edge to the interior of the outer lip and the columella, and a brown interior of the aperture. Up to 35 mm. We have found it only at Masirah. Rare.

Vexillum acuminatum
(Gmelin, 1791)

A narrow tapering shell with a very sharp pointed apex, deep sutures and cancellate sculpture. It is dark grey in color, with a pale line below the sutures. The inner edge of the outer lip is dark brown, the interior of the aperture bluish-white and the columella dark brown with three to four strong light colored plications. Up to 40 mm. Distribution general in sand at and below the low tide level. Fairly common.

Family **Harpidae**

The shells of this family are certain finalists in any beauty contest for molluscs! Their bright colors and well defined axial ribs are truly astonishing. The shells are ovate with a very wide aperture which occupies three-quarters the length of the shell. They have a very short spire. No operculum. No posterior canal. Smooth columella. They usually live in deep water but are sometimes found in sand near the low tide level. The animal is carnivorous.

Harpa amouretta
Roeding, 1798

A gorgeous little shell with the typical well defined axial ribs of the Harpa family. Up to 60 mm. The colors are various shades of black and brown on a creamy background. Aperture white inside, flushed with brown. We have found this only at Masirah. Rare.

Harpa ventricosa
Lamarck, 1816

This species is more rotund than *Harpa amouretta* and the axial ribs are more widely spaced and have sharp triangular apices. The colors are predominantly white, pink and brown. Up to 90 mm. We have found this only at Masirah. Rare.

Family **Volutidae**
A very colorful and variable family, most members of
which are of great beauty and much prized by
collectors. Most species have a characteristic bulbous
apex. Carnivorous.

Festilyria festiva
(Lamarck, 1811)

A rare member of this family,
with longitudinal ribs, strongly
shouldered, and strikingly
marked with brown on orange
and pink. The interior of the
aperture, which is more than
half the length of the shell, is
ivory and the columella is ivory,
with a dark brown blotch at the
anterior; it has fine plications
and two strong ones at the
anterior. Up to 140 mm. It is
presumed to live in deep water –
it is certainly not a shallow water
species. Dead specimens have
been found on beaches at
Masirah and at several
uninhabited islands off Oman's
southern coast. Rare.

Family **Cancellariidae (Nutmeg Shells)**

Short-spired with somewhat triangular apertures, folded columellas, posterior and anterior canals, with or without an umbilicus. No operculum. The name "Cancellaria" is suggested by the cancellate (latticelike) sculpture. We have read that the radula structure of this family suggests that the animals feed on soft-bodied organisms on the ocean floor.

Trigonostoma costifera
(Sowerby, 1833)

Ivory or pale brownish shell with very steep concave shoulders and fine sharp well-spaced axial ribs crossed by fine spiral threads. There is a deep umbilicus, the columella is inclined to the right and is plicate, the interior of the aperture is ridged and often streaked with orange-brown, there is a marked tooth-like projection at the posterior edge of the aperture. Up to 20 mm. Distribution general. Rare.

Cancellaria melanostoma
Sowerby, 1833

Shell with rounded whorls sculptured with fine axial and spiral ridges, deep sutures and a sharp-tipped apex. The color is orange-brown banded spirally with white, the columella is pale orange-brown and has two strong teeth or folds, the interior of the aperture is strongly ridged. Up to 40 mm. Distribution general. Rare.

Family **Marginellidae**

This is a group of predominantly small shells, many species being less than one-quarter inch in size. The aperture is usually narrow with a thickened outer lip. The spire is small and sometimes even sunken. As is the case with Cowries, the surface of the shell is glossy due to the mantle which covers the living shell. No operculum. The animal has a large foot and is a sand-dweller.

Marginella obscura
Reeve 1865

The color of this species is a bright orange which is clearly seen when it is wet. The thickened outer lip is brown and white alternately. Up to 15 mm, except at Masirah where we have found specimens up to 24 mm. This species, unlike many members of the Marginella family, lives beneath rocks and stones, and can only be found by turning over the stones at low tide. Often eight or ten specimens can be found beneath a single rock.
Distribution general. Common.

Marginella pergrandis
Clover, 1973

A very low-spired species, purplish-pink in color, faintly banded and flecked with pale marks. The columella has four strong plications. The interior of the aperture which extends four-fifths the length of the shell is violet. Up to 26 mm. This species was originally discovered by the authors in 1972 after which it was sent to Mr. Phillip W. Clover, who is a specialist in this family and who published the first description in 1973. Distribution general, but more common at Masirah than elsewhere. Rare.

Superfamily **Conacea**
Family **Turridae (Turret or Tower Shells)**
The shells in this family are generally fusiform in shape
with a long spire and a long or short siphonal canal.
They have a slit or depression on the outer lip, between
the suture and the periphery of the body whorl which is
called the "turrid slit" or "turrid notch". The
operculum is leaf shaped and horny. The name
"Turridae" is well chosen for many of these species
resemble the spiral towers we call turrets. Most species
have an elegant shape, sculptured with nodules and
spiral cords; sometimes the ornamentation is striking.

The animal has a venom gland and is carnivorous.
The classification of the genera in this family is subject
to a great deal of discussion. We have followed the
classification suggested by Dr. James H. McClean.

Crassispira species

A spirally ridged shell, brown in
color with paler color on the
ridges. There is a band of weak
tubercules around the shoulder
of each whorl and a strong ridge
above the suture. Interior of
aperture and columella creamy
pink. Aperture about two fifths
the length of shell. Up to
45 mm. Masirah only. Rare.

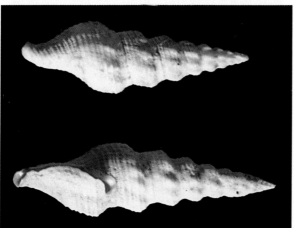

Crassispira cf. **flavidulus**
(Lamarck, 1822)

A typical Turrid with its tower-
like spire. The color is pale ivory,
the interior of the aperture being
pale pink. The shell is spirally
ridged with weak tubercules
around the shoulder. The
aperture is about one-third the
length of the shell. Up to 65 mm.
We have found it only at
Masirah. Rare.

Crassispira griffithi
(Gray, 1834)

A turreted shell with angular shoulders which have pale nodules around the periphery. The body whorl is spirally ridged, white on brown. The aperture is about two-fifths the length of the shell, the interior is pale brown; the turrid notch is deep. The columella is smooth and shining. Up to 55 mm. Its elegant shape and sculpture make it a special shell. The small operculum is horny. We have found it only at Masirah. Rare.

Crassispira species

A tall-spired shell with angular sloping shoulders which are ridged or fluted. The aperture is about one-third the length of the shell and is blotched brown inside. The columella is white and glossy. The exterior is sculptured with fine spiral threads; there is a coarse spiral cord immediately below the suture, which is marked with dark brown and cream and the base of the body whorl is also marked with dark brown, the rest of the shell is of a creamy color marked with pale brown. Up to 55 mm. It probably lives below the low-tide level since we have only found specimens which have been washed up on the beach at Masirah. Rare. We have not been able to identify this species to date.

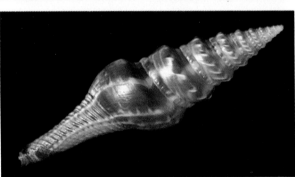

Turricula catena
(Reeve 1843)

This is an Erythraean species which has not been found outside the area to date – the distribution appears to be confined to the Red Sea, North Arabian Sea and the Gulfs. A tall-spired shell, the aperture about two-fifths the length. The siphonal canal is slightly curved at the tip. There is a nodulose cord below the suture. The whorls are rounded and smooth except for some very fine spiral striae. The color pattern is cloudy red flames on a lighter background. It differs from *Turricula tornata fulminata* in being much narrower. Up to 55 mm. Distribution general but more common at Masirah. Rare.

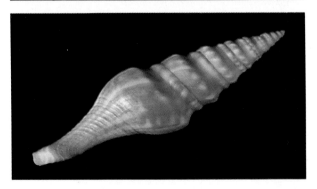

Turricula tornata fulminata
(Kiener, 1839–40)

Much broader than *Turricula catena* and with smooth sides, not with rounded whorls. The color pattern is similar. The aperture is almost longer than the spire. The cord below the suture is not nodulose. Up to 70 mm. We have found this species only at Masirah. Rare.

Drillia cecchi
Jousseaume

A narrow high-spired ivory colored shell with fine spiral ridges and a cord-like ridge below the suture. It has oblique rounded longitudinal ribs. The aperture is about two-fifths the length of the shell. The turrid notch is at the top of the aperture and is shallow, the siphonal canal is short and comparatively wide. Up to 20 mm. We have found it only at Masirah. Rare.

Gemmula unedo
(Kiener, 1839–40)

A spirally ridged shell with alternating brown and white dashes on the ridges, strongly keeled at the shoulder of each whorl. The aperture is about half the length of the shell. Up to 95 mm. This species is a sand dweller. Distribution general. Rare.

Turridrupa cincta
(Lamarck, 1822)

A beautiful little shell, broad with a tapering spire, emphatic spiral ridges, a small aperture and no marked siphonal canal. The turrid notch is small. The color is predominantly white. Up to 35 mm. It lives in sandy areas in the intertidal zone. We have found it only at Masirah. Rare.

Family **Conidae**
All Cones are conical in shape, and most have a long
narrow aperture. They are covered with a thin or thick
periostracum which comes off easily when the shell is
placed in bleach for a few minutes. All Cones have a
horn-like operculum which is usually small and narrow.

Because of their exceptional beauty and variability,
the Cones hold a special place in the hearts of most
collectors. No one knows how many valid species exist,
because hundreds of synonymic names have been given
by many authors. The experts seem to agree that there
are about 400 different species.

Most Cones are found in shallow water where they
frequently live beneath rocks or in rock crevices.
However, some species can be obtained only by
dredging in deeper water. Cones feed on worms, fish
and other molluscs. They have a special apparatus
which can be likened to a harpoon with which they
literally spear their prey, injecting a neuro-toxic
substance which paralyzes the victim. Some Cones,
such as *Conus geographus*, have been known to cause
human deaths. In Oman, two species are known to be
dangerous, i.e. *Conus textile* and *Conus pennaceus*. Species
such as this must be handled with extreme caution, and
should always be grasped from the shoulder of the shell
or else a protective glove should be used. These shells
should never be placed on the palm of the hand, or in
the pocket of a swimming suit, as they have been known
to sting through material and plastic.

Some immature forms of the Strombus family are not
infrequently mistaken for Cones.

Conus tessulatus
Born, 1778

A heavy, white shell with a low
channelled spire. It is patterned
with orange to crimson
rectangular blotches and
sometimes dashes. There are
orange or red blotches on the
spire. Up to 70 mm. Distribution
general. Uncommon.

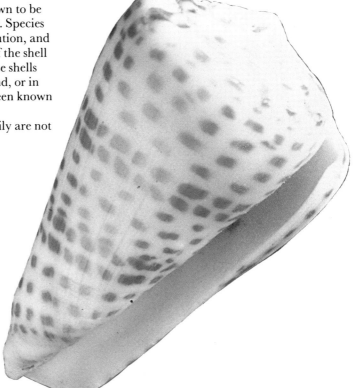

Conus coronatus
Gmelin, 1791

A short, wide shell with slightly convex sides, angled shoulders, a moderately high, coronate spire and fine spiral ridges towards the base of the body whorl. The background is bluish to pinkish grey, marked with dashes of darker color and sometimes showing one or two paler bands. The interior of the aperture is white, edged with pale brown. Up to 40 mm. Distribution general. Common.

Conus ebraeus
Linnaeus, 1758

A short, heavy chunky shell with a low, slightly coronate spire, rounded shoulders and convex sides. Sometimes there are fine spiral ridges towards the base. The background is white marked by rather rectangular black spots in rows. The interior of the aperture is white. Up to 35 mm. We have found this species only at Masirah. Rare.

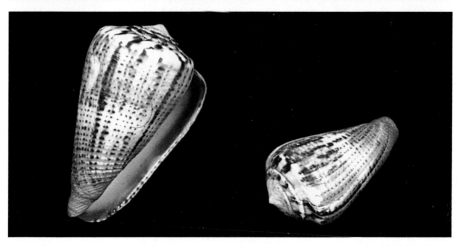

Conus biliosus
Roeding, 1798

A heavy, straight-sided, broad shell with a low, flat, slightly coronate spire and rounded shoulders. The body whorl has weak spiral ridges, more pronounced towards the anterior. The ground color varies from bluish-grey to brown with irregular rows of darker dots and dashes. Sometimes a paler central band may be present. The edge of the inner lip is brown, the aperture purple within. Up to 55 mm. We have found this species only at Masirah. Rare.

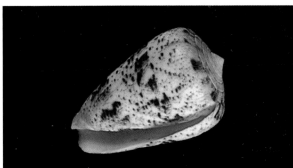

Conus zeylanicus
Gmelin, 1791

A heavy, solid shell with slightly convex sides, rounded shoulders and a low to medium spire. There are dark blotches in two bands with variously scattered dots and dashes between, brown on ivory. The aperture is ivory to pale purple-pink. Up to 70 mm. We have found it only at Masirah. Uncommon.

Conus musicus
Hwass, 1792

This species has often been called *Conus pusillus* Lamarck. It is a small heavy, chunky shell with a low spire, rounded shoulders and nearly straight sides, occasionally with fine spiral ridges on the body whorl. The background is whitish, variously dotted with brown or black spots or dashes in rows. The interior of the aperture is purple. Up to 30 mm. Distribution general. Rare.

Conus taeniatus
Hwass, 1792

A heavy shell with a low, sometimes coronate spire and convex sides. The background is bluish or greyish, marked with strong dark and white dashes in rows. The interior of the aperture is purplish with a pale band in the center.

Conus taeniatus lives in a special type of habitat with relatively flat rocks divided by crevices which are filled with sand, in which the cones can be found, often three or four specimens together. Sometimes a specimen of *Conus coronatus* will be found side by side with a *Conus taeniatus*. Up to 50 mm, the largest specimens being from Masirah. Distribution general. Uncommon.

Conus ardisiaceus
Kiener, 1845

A light-weight shell with convex sides, moderately rounded shoulders and a low spire culminating in a pointed apex. The anterior third of the body whorl is quite strongly spirally ridged. The columella is almost always brown at the tip and straight. The background color is bluish ivory, variously patterned with brown to a greater or lesser degree and there are irregular spiral rows of dark dots over the body whorl. The interior of the aperture is edged with pale color and is violet within, deeper at the posterior. Up to 50 mm. We have found this only at Masirah and Salalah. Common locally.

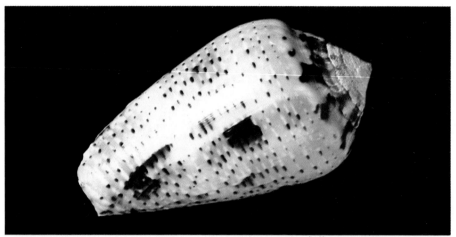

Conus nigropunctatus
Sowerby, 1857

This is a species very difficult to separate from *Conus achatinus* and is possibly only a variant. It is smaller and is characterized by the dark spots along the angle of the shoulder. Otherwise it resembles *Conus achatinus*. Up to 50 mm. Distribution probably general. Uncommon.

Conus boschi
Clover, 1972

One of the smaller members of the Cone family, with an unusual design which is reminiscent of a brick wall and a conspicuous, upstanding apex. The interior of the aperture has a purple tinge. Up to 35 mm. We discovered this species in the late 1960's and it was described and named in 1972, thus proving that new natural history species are still waiting to be found and described. We have always found live specimens in sandy silt in shallow water in protected areas, only at Masirah. Rare.

Conus achatinus
Hwass, 1792

A moderately light-weight, pyriform shell with a low spire and a sharp apex. The color and pattern are extremely variable, usually in shades of blue-grey and purple-brown. There are spiral pale lines punctuated with dark spots. The inner edge of the lip is dark and the aperture is bluish-grey. Up to 60 mm. Distribution general, under rocks in sand, partially buried. Uncommon. We follow Kohn (1978) in considering that this species is not a synonym of *Conus monachus* Linnaeus.

Conus generalis maldivus
Hwass, 1792

A long, slender, heavy shell with
concave sides and a sharply
concave spire with an elevated
apex. The pattern is of brown
lines on white, often with a
central white band. The spire is
white with brown dashes. The
aperture is suffused with purple
brown at the tip. Up to 70 mm.
We have found this species at
Masirah, where it is uncommon,
and Muscat, where it is rare.

Conus lemniscatus
Reeve, 1849

This shell has been more
commonly known as *Conus
traversianus* Smith, which is a
synonym. A slender, elongate
shell with straight or slightly
concave sides and a concave
spire terminating in a
prominent, sharp apex. The
body whorl is spirally striate,
especially the anterior third. The
background color is usually
bluish-white or cream patterned
with spiral lines of brown and
white dashes and variously
blotched with brown. The
interior of the aperture pale,
sometimes banded brown, the
anterior of the columella dark.
Occasionally we have found
specimens which are almost
uniformly orange-brown,
patterned with rows of pale
dashes. Up to 45 mm. We have
found this species only at
Masirah, in shallow water
between stones. Relatively rare.

Conus kermadecensis
Iredale, 1913

A chubby, moderately heavy shell with a concave or slightly stepped spire. It is banded with light brown in continuous or broken streaks on an ivory background. There are spiral rows of small dots present which may need a magnifying glass to detect. The spire is patterned with brown dashes. Many specimens have a violet blush in the aperture. We have noticed that this species is prone to deformity. Up to 60 mm. We have found this shell only on the east coast of Masirah where it is locally moderately common, dead.

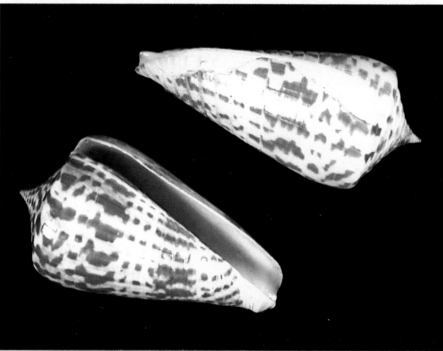

Conus inscriptus
Reeve, 1843

Conus adenensis Smith is a synonym. It is an elongated, heavy shell with slightly convex sides and a pronounced twist of the columella at the anterior. It has a low, concave spire. This species has a delicate appearance; the spiral rows of rectangular brown dots are interspersed with other rows of irregular brown patches on an ivory background. Up to 70 mm. We have had live specimens dredged from about 200 feet off Muscat. Distribution general. Rare.

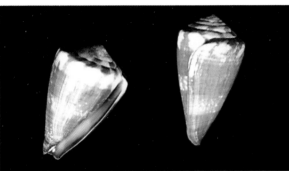

Conus rattus
Hwass, 1792

A chunky shell with squarish white blotches round the shoulder. The color is a shiny dark brown with bluish-white flecks and sometimes a paler band in the center. The interior of the aperture is banded with purple and edged with brown. Up to 62 mm. Distribution general. Rare.

Conus virgo
Linnaeus, 1758

A heavy, long, narrow shell with slightly rounded shoulders and a low, flat spire. The body whorl is finely striate, especially at the anterior. The color is ivory to cream with violet at the base and inside the tip of the white interior of the aperture. Up to 140 mm. Distribution general. Uncommon.

Conus namocanus
Hwass, 1792

A heavy, low-spired shell. The shoulder and spire have rectangular blotches of white. The color is pale to dark to reddish brown. The body whorl has encircling dark brown lines and usually there is a pale band round the centre. Up to 120 mm. We have found this species only at Salalah and Masirah. Moderately common locally.

Conus vexillum
Gmelin, 1791

The variety of this species that we have in Oman is *Conus vexillum sumatrensis* Hwass, 1792. It is a large, heavy, straight-sided shell with a very low spire. The background color is white with two bands of brown and strongly marked with dark brown longitudinal, irregular lines. The interior of the aperture is white. Up to 90 mm. This species is particularly prone to growth scars and defects. Distribution general. Rare.

Conus flavidus
Lamarck, 1822

A wider and shorter shell than
Conus virgo with a flat spire and
more angled shoulders. It is
characterized by its yellow color
with a paler central band and
purple tip. The interior of the
aperture is banded purple. Up to
60 mm. Next to *Conus coronatus*
this is the most common cone
living in Oman. It is to be found
in shallow water under rocks.
Distribution general. Very
common.

Conus terebra thomasi
Sowerby, 1881

A narrow, thick, heavy shell
with a flattish, smooth spire and
deep sutures. The surface is
finely striate. The color is ivory
with two wide bands of pinkish
cream and the aperture is white.
The periostracum is thick, heavy
and dark. This Erythraean
subspecies is broader and
heavier than the typical *Conus
terebra*. Up to 70 mm. We have
found it at Muscat, Salalah and
Masirah, in sand. Rare.

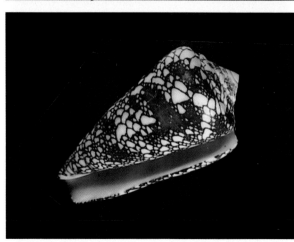

Conus pennaceus
Born, 1780

A straight-sided, heavy shell
with rounded shoulders and a
characteristic needle-sharp apex
in fresh specimens. The pattern
of pale tent-shaped markings on
dark chestnut is very variable.
The interior of the aperture is
bluish-white. Up to 80 mm. The
underside of the animal's foot is
brownish grey and the proboscis
is black, white and red. *Conus
pennaceus* lives under or between
rocks, half buried in the sand.
Distribution general. Fairly
common. This is one of the
species which can be poisonous
to human beings. Accordingly,
one should always pick up the
shell by the back near the spire
or preferably use a protective
glove to handle it.

Under no circumstances
should the live shell be placed on
the palm of the hand or in a
pocket where it could sting. The
experts do not always agree on
the identification of this species,
as the *Conus omaria/pennaceus*
complex can be confusing.

Conus quercinus
Solander, 1786

A thick, heavy, pyriform shell with angled shoulders and a flat to concave spire, often culminating in a sharp point. The color is bright yellow with pale brown spiral lines and a pale central band. The interior of the aperture is white. Up to 90 mm. We have found it in sandy areas but not near rocks. Distribution general. Uncommon.

Conus striatus
Linnaeus 1758

A medium-weight, cylindrical shell with tapered shoulders and a channelled, stepped spire. The body whorl is characterized by the incised spiral striations which give the shell its name. The pattern is pale to dark brown on white or pink. Up to 93 mm. Distribution general. Rare.

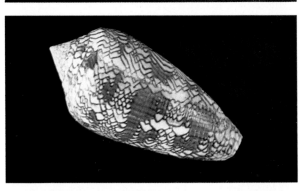

Conus textile
Linnaeus, 1758

A light weight, somewhat cylindrical shell with a moderately low, pointed spire. The tent-shaped markings, which vary in size and pattern are ivory on orange-brown, and there are longitudinal dark lines crossing the pattern. The interior of the aperture is white and the periostracum is thin, yellow and transparent. The proboscis is red, white and black. Up to 120 mm. It is usually found in sand under rocks. Distribution general. Like *Conus pennaceus* this species can be poisonous to humans and should be handled with care, as previously described. We have seen one very large living specimen which was captured in Muscat harbor by Mr. Fred (Rick) Luther.

Conus betulinus
Linnaeus, 1758

A thick, heavy, pyriform shell with a depressed spire and broad, rounded shoulders. One could almost imagine that the designers of space modules got their inspiration from the shape of this shell! The anterior is strongly ridged and the background is white to yellow, patterned with spiral rows of dots. Up to 140 mm. We have found it in sand or silt, on the open beach or in pockets of sand on reefs. This species is poisonous but not lethal to humans. Distribution general. Uncommon.

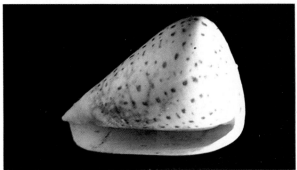

Family **Terebridae (Auger Shells)**

The members of this family are often called Auger
Shells because of their obvious resemblance to an auger
or drill. The shells are long and narrow with a high
pointed spire, many whorls, a small aperture and a
horny thin operculum. Their slender shape is well
adapted for their predatory habits since they can
burrow through sand easily. They can be found in sand
in shallow water, often leaving a trail behind them on
the sand above as they burrow through it. They are
carnivorous. Some species have a poison gland; the
venom is capable of killing their prey but, unlike the
Conus family, this venom is not dangerous to man.

Duplicaria duplicata
(Linnaeus, 1758)

The shell has a deep spiral
groove below the suture and fine
longitudinal grooves. The color
varies from grey to purplish-grey
or cream and there is a row of
dark dots above the suture. Up
to 70 mm. Distribution general.
Common.

Terebra cingulifera
Lamarck, 1822

Each whorl has two fine grooves.
There is a deep suture and the
shoulders are angled. The
surface is finely longitudinally
striate. Up to 75 mm.
Distribution general.
Uncommon.

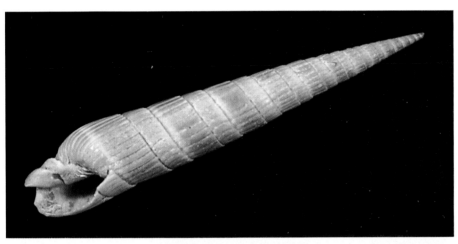

Duplicaria species

This species is similar to *Duplicaria duplicata*, but is consistently heavier, larger, uniformly colored and the longitudinal grooves are closer together. The color is blue-grey. Up to 110 mm. It can be found in the sand at low tide all along the Batinah coast. Distribution general. Common.

Impages hectica
(Linnaeus, 1758)

A slender, glossy shell with a slight sutural groove and fine wavy striations diagonally across the whorls. There is a coarse columella plait. It is unusually beautiful with a variable design of fine reddish-brown longitudinal lines on ivory or white and usually with a row of darker dots or dashes below the suture. Up to 65 mm. Distribution general. Common.

Subula maculata
(Linnaeus 1758)

The shell is large, heavy and thick with a glossy surface and a striking design of dark brown on ivory or cream. The aperture is small in comparison with the length of the shell. Up to 170 mm. We have found this species only at Masirah, where it is rare although it is common elsewhere in the Indo-Pacific.

Subclass **Opisthobranchia**
Order **Tectibranchia**

Superfamily **Acteonacea (Bullacea)**
Family **Acteonidae (Pupidae)**
Small to medium sized shells with spiral ridges and
folded columellas; operculate.

Acteon eloiseae
Abbott, 1973

This is a very colorful and
attractive species, dramatically
patterned with bold rose-colored
black-bordered squarish blotches
on an ivory ground. The first
reaction of many people on
seeing the shell for the first time
is that it has been painted. The
operculum is chitonous. Up to
38 mm. It is named for Mrs.
Eloise Bosch, one of the authors
of this book. Thus far *Acteon
eloiseae* has only been found at
Masirah where it is rare.

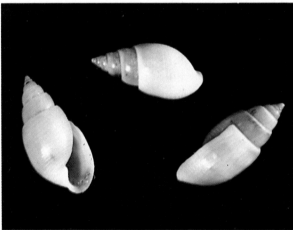

Bullina lineata
(Wood, 1828)

A pretty, fragile shell with a low
spire and a wide aperture. It is
delicately colored pink with
deeper pink lines and markings.
Up to 20 mm. We have found it
in areas where sand and mud
mix. Distribution general. Rare.

Acteon siebaldii
Reeve, 1842

A white shell with spiral grooves,
angled shoulders and deep
sutures. There is a single fold on
the columella. Up to 20 mm.
This species lives in areas where
sand and mud mix. Distribution
general. Rare.

Acteon affinis
(A. Adams, 1854)

A small solid shell, spirally
ridged and marked with dark
dashes on a white ground. The
foot and head of the animal is
white. Up to 25 mm.
Distribution general. Common.

Gastropoda

Family **Hydatinidae (Aplustridae)**

Globular, fragile shells with sunken spires. No
operculum. The aperture is large and often runs the
length of the shell. The animals live in sand.

Hydatina velum
(Gmelin, 1791)

Very similar to *Hydatina physis*,
except that the color is white and
the shell is encircled by a white
band edged with brown, and
brown bands at the top and
bottom. It has fine dark
longitudinal lines. Up to 35 mm.
Distribution general. Rare.

Hydatina physis
(Linnaeus, 1758)

The color is white with spiral
dark brown lines. The shells are
extremely fragile. Up to 35 mm.
Distribution general. Rare.

Family **Bullidae (Bubble Shells)**
Globular solid shells with sunken spires. No operculum.

Bullaria ampulla
(Linnaeus, 1758)

No beachcomber in Oman can fail to find specimens of this shell. It is varying in color, dark or light brown on a paler ground. Up to 60 mm. It lives in sand, emerging at night. Distribution general. Very common.

Family **Atyidae**
Cylindrical or globular shells with sunken spires.
Fragile.

Atys cylindrica
(Helbling, 1779)

A fragile, translucent white,
cylindrical shell with a sunken
spire. There are finely incised
spiral lines at the top and bottom
of the shell. Up to 12 mm.
Distribution general. Common,
dead.

Superfamily **Pyramidellacea**
Family **Pyramidellidae**

Long, slender, shiny shells with small apertures and
folded columellas. The animals are often parasitic on or
in other marine creatures.

Pyramidella sulcata
(A. Adams, 1860)

Shaped like *Pyramidella acus* but
not as colorful. It is an off-white
to fawn color with indefinite
orange-brown spots. Up to 50 mm.
We have found it in sandy
areas in the shallow sub-tidal
zone. Distribution general.
Rare.

Pyramidella acus
(Gmelin, 1791)

Smooth, bluish-ivory or creamy-
white in color, with rows of
brown blotches. It has a small
corneous operculum. Up to 50
mm. We have found this species
in sand in the shallow sub-tidal
zone. *Pyramidella maculosa*
Lamarck is a synonym.
Distribution general. Rare.

Order **Acoela (Notaspidea)**

Superfamily **Umbraculacea**
Family **Umbraculidae (Umbrella Shells)**
Flat or slightly domed shells covering only the top of the
animal which is very large, like a hat or umbrella.

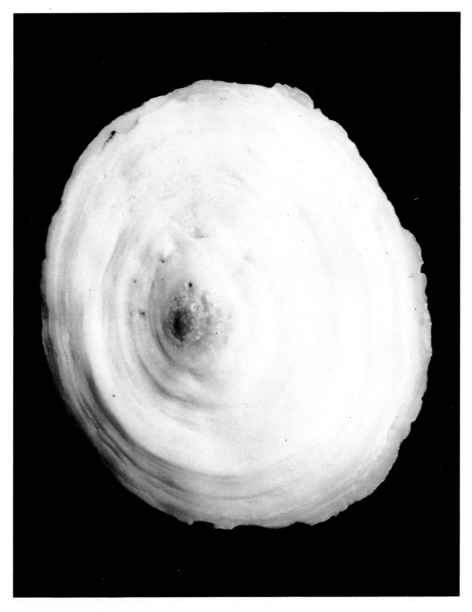

Umbraculum sinicum
(Gmelin, 1791)

The shell is a depressed dome
with the small apex a little off-
center. Upper surface is white or
ivory, sometimes stained yellow.
The interior is nacreous, with a
central brown muscle scar which
is radially ribbed. Up to 75 mm.
A synonym is *Umbraculum indicum*
Lamarck. We have found this
species only at Masirah. Rare.

Subclass **Pulmonata**
Order **Basommatophora**

Superfamily **Siphonariacea**
Family **Siphonariidae (False Limpets)**
Shells similar to those of the True Limpets, but there is
an internal groove for the siphon, indicated on the
exterior by a rib or enlarged rib.

Siphonaria tenuicostulata
Smith, 1903

Moderately domed shells, finely
ribbed, alternating ribs tending
to be a little coarser than the
intermediate ones. White ribs on
brown shells, sometimes
encrusted with lime. There is a
single, not a double rib over the
siphonal groove. Interior
nacreous, the edge of the shell
white and the rest of the interior
rich dark brown or light purple-
brown. Up to 15 mm. This
species can be found at low tide
in large numbers; as many as a
100 specimens can be found on
a single large rock. Sometimes
we found them right up against
one another but never on top of
one another. Distribution
general. Common.

Scaphapoda and Chitons

There are about 1,000 species in the Class Scaphapoda. They are the "tusk shells", so called because they resemble a miniature elephant's tusk. The Chitons are of the Class Amphineura, of which there are some 600 species. Normally they have eight shelly plates across the back, although aberrant members with seven or nine plates have been found.

Class **Scaphopoda**
Family **Dentaliidae**
Tusk shaped shells. Open at both ends.

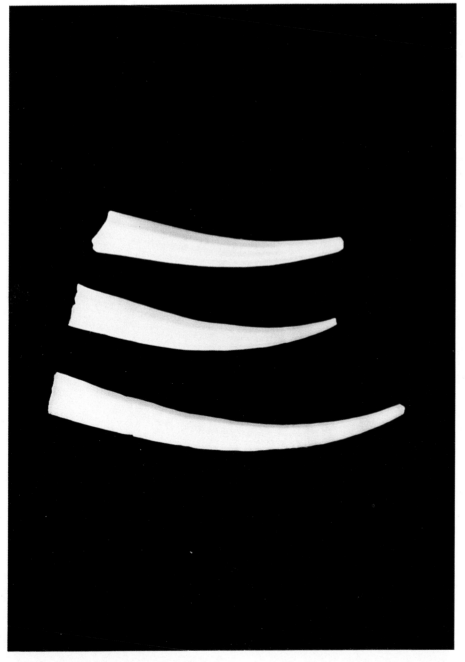

Dentalium octangulatum
Donovan, 1803

Shell usually octagonal in section but occasionally ones are found which are seven or nine-sided. Up to 60 mm. Distribution general. Very common.

Class **Amphineura (Polyplacophora)**
Order **Teleoplacophora**

Family **Chitonidae (Coat of Mail Shells)**
Oval, flattened animals, with eight over-lapping plates
on the dorsal surface instead of a single or double shell.
The plates are embedded in a tough structure called the
girdle. Usually to be found from the high-tide level to
moderately shallow water, on or under rocks, stones or
similar hard substrates. They are vegetarian, feeding
mainly on algae. There are several·species of Chitons to
be found in Oman but most are small and present
problems in identification.

Acanthopleura haddoni
Winckworth, 1927

This has been recorded
incorrectly from this area as
Acanthopleura spiniger (Sowerby)
but this latter is narrower and
has a very spiny girdle. No one
can fail to find this large chiton
in most rocky areas, in large
colonies and in all stages of
growth from the youngest to the
largest old eroded adults, up to
70 mm in length. The girdle is
covered with fine scales, giving a
shagreened appearance, and is
striped in pale and darker grey.
The valves or plates have a
"beak" in the centre of each
where it overlaps the next valve.
Younger animals show a degree
of sculpturing on the valves, but
this is usually indistinct and
eroded and the general color is
brownish grey, often encrusted
with lime or other deposits.
Distribution general. Abundant.

Bivalvia

There are about 10,000 species in this Class. They have two shelly
halves, connected by a hinge ligament, muscles and interlocking teeth.

Class **Bivalvia**
Subclass **Pteriomorpha**
Order **Arcoida**

Superfamily **Arcacea**
Family **Arcidae (Ark Shells)**
Shells with a more or less straight hinge line with many
fine interlocking teeth rather like a comb. This is known
as a taxodont hinge. External ligament. Equal muscle
scars. No pallial sinus. Most species live anchored by a
byssus. Many have a brown periostracum, often partly
eroded and missing.

Anadara rufescens
(Reeve, 1844)

Equivalve, inequilateral, umbos
close together. Fine ribs
radiating from the umbos, the
interspaces having a cancelled
appearance. The shell is white,
with a reddish-brown fan-shaped
streak of color radiating from the
umbos and fading towards the
anterior edge. Up to 85 mm.
Found attached to solid objects
at or below low tide level.
Distribution general. Common.

Anadara ehrenbergi
(Dunker, 1868)

Equivalve, inequilateral shells,
with the radiating ribs and
interspaces being of equal size
and crossed by fine spiral ridges.
Color ivory to cream. Up to
90 mm. Distribution general.
Rare.

Anadara uropigimelana
(Bory de St. Vincent, 1824)

Inflated, equivalve, inequilateral shells with the umbos moderately close together, the area between the umbos dark brown. The radiating ribs are flattened and separated by very narrow interspaces. The shape is squarish, rounded at the anterior and angular at the posterior. Up to 80 mm. Found attached by a byssus to rocks and in crevices. Distribution general. Very common.

Anadara secticostata
(Reeve, 1844)

Equivalve, inequilateral, shell elongated with the umbos fairly close together and towards the anterior. The anterior edge is rounded and the posterior angular and straight. The radiating ribs are double, with the interspaces being smooth. Color white. Up to 90 mm. Found attached to rocks at low-tide level. Distribution general. Rare.

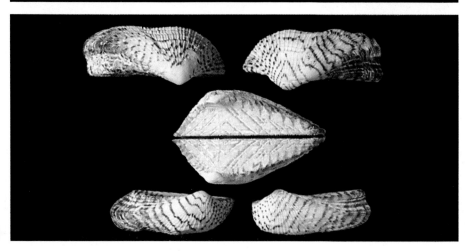

Arca ventricosa
(Limarck, 1819

A very elongate, coarsely ribbed shell, with prominent umbos fairly wide apart near the rounded anterior, and a strong ridge extending from the umbos to the posterior ventral margin. It is creamy with red-brown zigzag markings. There is a pronounced gap for the byssus in the ventral edge. It is a typical "Ark Shell" and looks very much like a flat topped boat. Up to 80 mm. We have found it at Sur, Muscat, Salalah and Masirah. Uncommon.

Barbatia fusca
(Bruguière, 1789)

Inequivalve, very inequilateral, irregularly shaped shells, coarsely ridged and covered with a coarse hairy periostracum in life. The shape is erratic due to the crevices in which they live, but the umbos are near the anterior. Coarsely ridged and is brownish, the interior white, flushed with brown. Distribution general. Common.

Barbatia helblingii
(Bruguière, 1789)

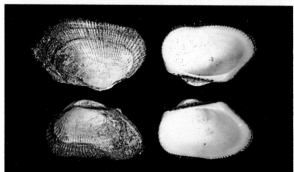

Inequivalve, inequilateral, irregularly shaped shells, the umbos near the anterior, the area between them being coarsely grooved. The ribs are moderately fine and sometimes divided. Under the coarse hairy periostracum the shell is white, as is the interior. Up to 60 mm. The animal remains in one place for its lifetime secured by the byssus within a deep crevice or under rocks. Distribution general. Common. *Barbatia decussata* (Sowerby) is a probable synonym.

Barbatia obliquata
(Wood, 1828)

A pronouncedly elongated shell, the umbos very close together and almost at the pointed anterior, the posterior end being broader with the posterior edge slanting and rounded at the ventral edge. The periostracum is finely hairy, the shell brownish and almost smooth and glossy. The interior is flushed with brown. Up to 75 mm. Found attached to rocks or in crevices. Distribution general but more common at Salalah than at Muscat, where it is rare.

Acar plicata
(Dillwyn, 1817)

A small strong shell, equivalve, inequilateral, pinkish in color, with the umbos close together, rounded anterior, and a strong ridge from the umbos to the posterior ventral edge. The sculpture is cancellate, except for the heart-shaped (when viewed from the posterior) part between the ridges which has wavy lines. There is a small ventral gap for the byssus. Up to 22 mm. Often ten or twelve specimens can be found under one stone in shallow water. Distribution general. Abundant.

Family **Cucullaeidae**

Very similar to Arcidae. Anterior margin straight, posterior rounded. Anterior muscle scar borne upon a shelf-like projection from the interior of the shell.

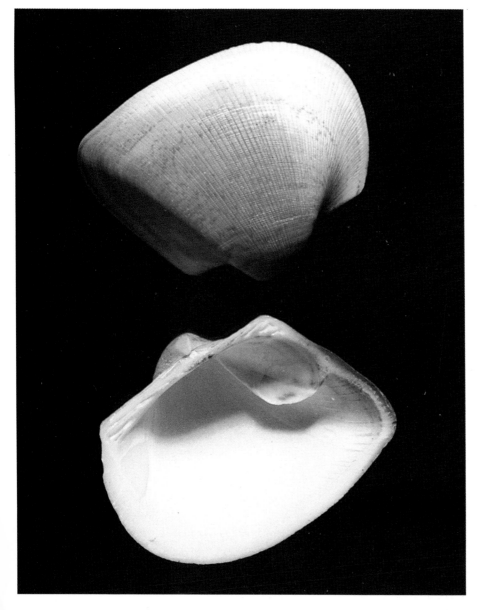

Cucullaea labiata
(Solander, 1786)

Shell heart-shaped when both paired valves are viewed from end on. Very finely ribbed, the ribs crossed by extremely fine striations. Brownish-pink in color fading to white at the edges. Interior white except for some flecks on the muscle scars and at the edges of the shell. 100 mm. We have found only one specimen at Masirah.

Superfamily **Limopsacea**
Family **Glycymerididae**
Circular shells, with the hinge teeth in an arc and like a
coarse comb. Ligament external. Muscle scars equal.
No pallial sinus.

Glycymeris lividus
Reeve, 1844

Glycymeris heroicus Melvill is a
synonym. An inflated, rounded
shell, with central umbos and
fine radiating ribs. The hinge
line is rounded like a bow and
the teeth are large. The color is
brown, but the shades vary from
light brown to a deep orange-
brown. Up to 80 mm. The
animal lives in sand in shallow
water. Distribution probably
general but we have found it
only on the Batinah coast
beaches near Muscat.
Uncommon.

**Glycymeris pectunculus
maskatensis**
(Melvill, 1897)

A moderately heavy, not very
inflated, rounded shell with
central umbos and the radiating
ridges bifurcating or dividing
towards the anterior edge. The
hinge teeth are large. The
background color is white,
decorated with brown lines,
sometimes in a chevron
formation. The interior is tinged
with brown. Up to 45 mm. This
species lives in sand and we have
found it in shallow water.
Distribution general.
Uncommon.

Order **Mytiloida**

Superfamily **Mytilacea**
Family **Mytilidae (Mussels)**

Equivalve, inequilateral shells, with or without hinge teeth. The umbo usually at or near the anterior end. They frequently live in large colonies in groups or banks. To avoid being traumatized by waves and ocean currents they attach themselves to fixed objects by means of a threadlike byssus which is very strong and difficult to pull apart. Because many of the species are edible or are used as bait the Mussels are economically important.

Amygdalum japonicum
(Dunker, 1856)

Shell with weak umbos near the anterior end, which is short and with a rounded point, widening towards the posterior. Part of the surface with weak radiating ribs. Shell thin. Brownish periostracum over a bluish shell weakly patterned with wavy concentric markings. Up to 45 mm. Attached by a byssus. Distribution general. Common.

Modiolus philippinarum
(Hanley, 1843)

The umbo is near the straight anterior edge and from it a swelling ridge extends to the dorsal edge. The surface of the shell is sculptured with concentric growth striae. The exterior color is brown or purple brown on a bluish subsurface. The interior is nacreous, white streaked with purple. No hinge teeth. Up to 75 mm. Permanently attached by the byssus to rocks, piles or driftwood. Distribution general. Common.

Lithophaga cumingiana
(Reeve, 1857)

A long, cylindrical shell with umbos near anterior, the valves joined by a long fine ligament. The shells are rounded at anterior and posterior ends and have a straight ventral and pointed dorsal edge. From the posterior end calcareous extensions project: this calcareous deposit tends to cover much of the shell surface which has fine concentric growth striae and is brown. The interior is nacreous purplish. Up to 70 mm. The members of the genus Lithophaga live in soft rocks, excavating burrows by means of an acid secretion and spend their lives in these burrows; they can only be found by breaking open the rocks. Because of this habit they are called "rock-eaters". Distribution general. Common.

Mytilus viridis
Linnaeus, 1758

A typical mussel, with blunt umbos at the tip of the anterior end and widening towards the posterior. No anterior adductor muscle impression. Concentric growth striae. Brown to green in color, very variable. Up to 100 mm. Distribution general. Common.

Mytilus pictus
Born, 1778

Similar in shape to *Mytillus viridis*, this attractive mussel is brown, and patterned variously with dashes and other markings. The growth striae are coarse and tend to give the edge of the shell a rough irregular appearance. Up to 75 mm. We have found this species at Salalah, grouped in large banks in shallow water in close proximity to each other. Distribution appears to be confined to the south of Oman where it is common.

Family **Pinnidae (Pen Shells)**

Wedge-shaped, gaping shells, with nacreous interior; large posterior and small anterior muscle scar. Umbo at anterior. No hinge teeth. Ligament internal. Anchored in the substrate by a byssus, the pointed end down. The byssus of this group of shells is particularly fine and silky, that of the Mediterranean species being of a rich golden color. Historically, the people of Sicily used to weave an elegant golden fabric, the legendary "cloth-of-gold" from the supple and delicate threads in the byssus of the Mediterranean Pinna shells.

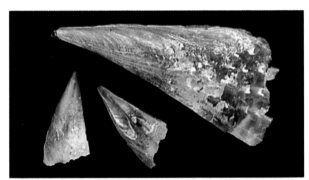

Pinna muricata
Linnaeus, 1758

Wedge-shaped, the anterior margin rather convex and the dorsal rather straight or concave. Shell moderately thin and keeled longitudinally, sculptured with radiating ribs from the umbo. Often the ribs have spines or scales. The posterior end of the shell which projects from the substrate is usually worn and damaged. The color is pale brown, variously marked with darker purplish brown. Internal nacreous region divided by a sulcus, the dorsal area being longer than the ventral. Hinge ligament black and extending from the anterior to the posterior part of the nacre. Up to 180 mm. Distribution general. Common.

Streptopinna saccata
(Linnaeus, 1758)

Juvenile specimens of this species may be difficult to distinguish from other species of Pinna but the adults are so contorted that they are easily identified. The dorsal margins and ventral margins often appear to be fused along a considerable part of their length (hence the name). The surface is sculptured by coarse ribs, the color is dull grey through tan to dark brown. The nacreous internal layer is smoky, and confined to a triangular area in the anterior dorsal part of the valves. Up to 160 mm. Distribution general. Common.

Atrina vexillum
(Born, 1778)

Shell wedge-shaped, becoming flag-shaped in older specimens with an extension to the ventral margin suggesting a flag blowing in the wind. The shell is moderately strong, usually dark and dull in color, and has obsolete ribs. The posterior muscle scar is very noticeable and bulges considerably in large specimens. The nacreous area occupies mostly the anterior part of the interior of the valves. The hinge ligament is very thick and black. Up to 180 mm. Distribution general. Common.

Order **Pteroida**

Superfamily **Pteriacea**
Family **Pteriidae (Pearl Mussels)**
Flattish shells with a straight hinge line and no hinge teeth. Interior nacreous, capable of producing pearls. Central muscle scar. No pallial sinus. With byssus.

Pteria marmorata
(Reeve, 1857)

Inequivalve shell with an elongated winglike extension of the straight hinge line. Exterior brown with radiating greenish rays. Interior highly nacreous. Up to 110 mm. The name "Pteria" meaning "wing" comes from the Greek language and is an appropriate name for these shells. We have found this species only at Masirah. Rare.

Pinctada margaritifera (Black-lipped Pearl Oyster)
(Linnaeus, 1758)

Shell without winglike extension to the hinge. Exterior greenish-brown to brown with radiating rays and broad radiating scaly ribs. The lamellae on the ribs may be numerous or worn, depending on the conditions of the locality in which the animal lives. The interior is highly nacreous, the nacreous area bordered by a black or dark edge. Up to 300 mm. Attached to a firm substrate by a byssus, often found in large colonies. Younger and smaller specimens can be found in water only a few feet in depth at low tide but the large specimens live at much greater depths. Distribution general. Common.

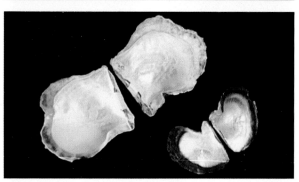

Pinctada radiata
(Leach, 1814)

This species is considered by many authorities to be *Pinctada vulgaris* Schumacher, 1817. Externally the appearance is very similar to that of *Pinctada margaritifera*, except that it is even more variable in color and the dark rays are often more pronounced, deep brown on pale fawn or yellow, and the shells are usually smaller. Internally they lack the dark border to the nacreous area. Up to 200 mm. Habitat as *Pinctada margaritifera*. Distribution general. Common. These two species are the famous pearl oysters which at one time provided a major industry at Bahrain and Muscat. Nowadays the development of cultured pearls has virtually destroyed the diving profession.

Family **Isognomonidae**
Straight hinge line with ligamental grooves or pits.
Nacreous interior. No pallial sinus. Byssus.

Isognomon legumen
(Gmelin, 1791)

Inequivalve, fragile pale-colored shells, irregular and elongated in shape, often damaged along the delicate edges. Inside it is mother of pearl. Up to 65 mm. Usually found on the undersurface of rocks in colonies. Distribution general. Common.

Family **Malleidae (Hammer Oysters)**

Hinge long and straight with the ligament in a triangular central pit. Pronounced lateral extensions of the hinge.

Malleus malleus
(Linnaeus, 1758)

An inequivalve, moderately thick shell with a T-shaped appearance, appropriately named since the valves and elongated wings so closely resemble a mallet. The shape is never the same in two different specimens. Externally dark in color, internally with a dark grey-blue central area and black muscle scars. Up to 180 mm. Found in shallow water attached to solid objects by a byssus. We have found this species only at Masirah. Uncommon. The first time a collector finds this shell he cannot help but look at it in complete disbelief that such a creature exists. Some people call them "bat wings".

Superfamily **Pectinacea**
Family **Pectinidae (Scallops)**
Equivalve or inequivalve rounded shells with "ears".
No hinge teeth. Ligament internal. Anterior ear usually
has a notch for the byssus. One muscle scar. There are
hundreds of species of Pectens distributed all over the
world. In some places they live in huge numbers,
packed together in banks, fixed by a byssus. Some
species can swim by clapping their valves together.
Those species which are edible are sold as "Scallops",
the adductor muscle being the part of the animal used
as food. Some Pectens are beautifully colored, thus
making them desirable collector's items.

Decatopecten plica
(Linnaeus, 1758)

The right valve is more convex
than the left, the hinge line is
short and the ears small. There
are usually five or six broad
striated radial ribs. The colors
are spectacular ranging from
white to brown to pink. Up to 45
mm. Distribution general.
Uncommon. Although the
animal is edible, it has never
become an acceptable food item
in Oman.

Pecten erythraeensis
(Sowerby, 1847)

The two valves are entirely
different, one being almost flat,
slightly convex, the other
extremely concave, so much so
that it resembles a rubber ball
cut in half. Eighteen to twenty
groove radial ribs are the
predominant sculpture.
Externally the color is patterns of
pink to white, internally it is
glossy white. Up to 60 mm.
Distribution general. Rare.

Chlamys senatorius
(Gmelin, 1791)

Both valves are nearly equal and convex. The anterior ear is longer than the posterior. The shell is nearly circular in shape with 30 to 40 shallow, scaly, radial ribs, the interspaces being as wide as the ribs. Up to 60 mm. The color is usually reddish brown to white. Distribution general. Uncommon.

Chlamys corallinoides
(d'Orbignyi, 1839)

Both valves convex, and with coarse, radiating uneven ribs, made rough by the abrupt concentric growth lines; because of this eccentric appearance identifying this species is easy, except in juveniles which have not yet reached the stage of developing the concentric ridges. Up to 60 mm. We have found this only at Masirah. Rare.

Chlamys townsendi
(Sowerby, 1895)

The left valve is more convex than the right, the ears are almost equal and the radiating ribs (20 to 30 in number) are very even and almost smooth, as are the interspaces. The shell is thick and heavy, almost round in shape. Up to 200 mm. Sometimes the larger specimens will weigh as much as six or seven pounds. The color is brown to reddish-brown. Distribution the southern coast of Oman and Masirah. Uncommon.

Chlamys ruschenbergerii
(Tryon, 1870)

Convex, nearly equal valves with 30 to 40 radial ribs, sculptured with scales. The color varies from brown to reddish-brown the interior is pale to deep purple, bordered with purple. Up to 95 mm. Distribution general. Common. This is by far the commonest Scallop living in Omani waters. It lives in association with rocks to which it attaches itself with a thread-like byssus. Sometimes we have found it under rock ledges. At Bunder Al Jisr, near Muscat, thousands of these animals cling to the rocks. When pulled away from the rock, they can swim by clapping their valves together.

Family **Plicatulidae**
Inequivalve, inequilateral shells, cemented to solid
objects by the right valve. Two cardinal teeth in each
valve, one muscle scar, ligament internal.

Plicatula imbricata
Menke, 1843

Some authorities consider this to
be a synonym of *Plicatula plicata*
(Linnaeus) from which it differs
in being patterned with dark
dots and dashes on the white
background. The edges are
serrated and interlocking and
the hinge teeth are conspicuous.
Up to 45 mm. Distribution
general. Abundant.

Family **Spondylidae (Thorny Oysters)**

Similar to Plicatulidae but with the radiating ribs more
or less sculptured with fronds or scales.

Spondylus exilis
Sowerby, 1895

Some authorities consider this to
be a synonym of *Spondylus
gaederopus* (Linnaeus). *Spondylus
townsendi* Melvill is also a
synonym. The shells are thick
and heavy, with inflated valves,
the upper valve being sculptured
with about four radial scaly
ridges, between each strong
radial rib. The ribs bear long or
short elaborate fronds. The
sculpture is very variable,
depending on the habitat, those
living in a sheltered environment
being more elaborately fronded
than those in an open area
subject to attack by heavy seas.
Up to 80 mm. The free edge of
the mantle has "eye spots",
which are sensitive to light.
(This also applies to most species
in the Pectinacea). The color
varies from purple to orange.

Superfamily **Anomiacea**
Family **Anomiidae (Jingle Shells or Saddle Oysters)**
Shiny, semi-translucent shells with the left valve nearly
flat and having an opening for the strong, coarse byssus
which anchors it to solid objects. No hinge teeth.

Anomia laqueata
Reeve, 1859

More solid and less fragile than
Anomia achaeus, the colors being
very variable, from cream to
pink or orange, and glossy
outside as well as in, with the
umbos less distinct. Up to 65
mm. Distribution general. Dead
upper valves are very common,
cast up on the beaches.

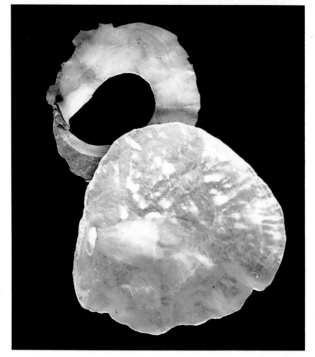

Anomia achaeus
Gray, 1849

Iridescent inside, the exterior
being dull with fine scaly ribs;
the umbos are distinct. The
valves are very fragile. The color
is greyish. Distribution general.
Rare. Up to 65 mm.

Superfamily **Limacea**
Family **Limidae (File Shells)**
Equivalve, usually inequilateral shells with no hinge teeth and an internal ligament. Most species have a roughened surface, hence the name "File Shells". The animals can swim by opening and closing the valves.

Lima sowerbyi
Deshayes, 1863

A triangular, inequilateral shell with a pointed umbo, one side being distinctly shorter than the other. The exterior of the shell has many radiating ridges which bear numerous spiny points such as a wood file would have. Up to 40 mm. The animals can attach themselves by a byssus, which can be detached at will. Distribution general. Rare.

Superfamily **Ostreacea**
Family **Ostreidae (Oysters)**
Inequivalve, inequilateral, strong heavy shells, usually
cemented to solid objects or to each other by the left
valve. All species have the ability to store water and
endure long periods exposed to the sun above the low
tide level.

Ostrea cristagalli
(Linnaeus, 1758)

This is sometimes called the
"Cock's Comb Oyster", an
obvious name for the shell with
its deep zigzag margins. Very
irregular in shape, but
unmistakeable. Up to 90 mm.
Distribution general. Common.

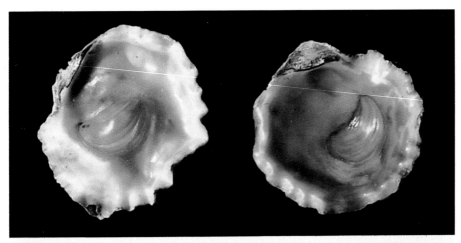

Alectryonella plicatula
(Gmelin, 1791)

In this area this species has been referred to as *Ostrea iridescens* Hanley which is a dubious species. The valves are usually flat and not very deep, the exterior is white and the interior white, often with a greenish tinge. It is extremely variable in shape. Up to 60 mm. Often found in the intertidal zone. Distribution general. Common.

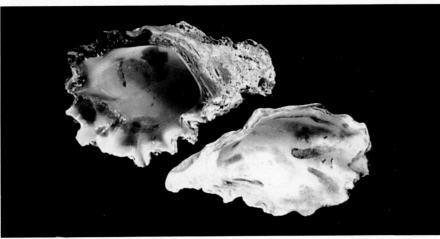

Ostrea cucullata
(Born, 1775)

Inequivalve, very irregularly shaped oysters, the valves sometimes very deep and sometimes almost flat. The lower valve adapts itself to the shape of the substrate, even growing projections to cling round an object such as a mangrove root. Interior white. Up to 85 mm. This species is excellent to eat and in Oman it is easy to enjoy a picnic with fresh oyster stew. Distribution general. Very common.

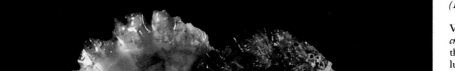
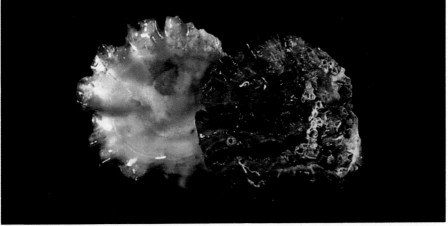

Hyotissa hyotis
(Linnaeus, 1758)

Very similar sometimes to *Ostrea cristagalli*, but distinguishable by the translucent almost luminescent quality of the interior, caused by the structure of the shell layers underlying the surface. Up to 120 mm. We have found this species only at Masirah. Uncommon.

Subclass **Heterodonta**
Order **Veneroida**

Superfamily **Lucinacea**
Family **Lucinidae**
Equivalve, inequilateral, usually rounded shells. Hinge
teeth arrangement varies. No pallial sinus. Internal
ligament.

Codakia tigerina
(Linnaeus, 1758)

The exterior of the shell has a
cancellated appearance, and is a
beautiful white. The interior is
yellow to yellow-white. Up to
80 mm. We have found it in sand
in shallow water. Distribution
general, but especially common
at Sur and the Khuriya Muriya
Islands. Common.

Family **Ungulinidae**

Roundish to oval shells, with unequal muscle scars,
usually smooth exterior. No pallial sinus.

Diplodonta ravayensis
Sturany, 1901

A moderately inflated shell,
sometimes so bloated that the
specimens are almost like a ball.
White, with faint irregularly
spaced concentric growth lines.
Up to 35 mm. Found in sand.
Distribution general.
Uncommon.

Superfamily **Chamacea**
Family **Chamidae (Jewel Boxes)**
Inequivalve, inequilateral shells, with spiral umbos,
cemented to solid objects by one valve. Ligament
external. Hinge teeth coarse and with grooves.

Chama pacifica
Broderip, 1834

This species has many synonyms.
The exterior is variously
ornamented with frills or spines
and is pink to purplish-pink,
when the color and ornament is
not obscured by marine deposits
or growths. The interior is white,
bordered with purple. The hinge
teeth are very strong and coarse
and have the appearance of
possessing a deep "V"-shaped
groove in the lower valve. Up to
65 mm. The animals live below
the low-tide level, cemented
strongly to rocks and so the shells
are mostly found as single valves,
cast up on the beaches after a
storm. Distribution general.
Probably common but seldom
found.
    The illustration shows the
interior view of upper and lower
valves – the latter with a small
specimen of the same species
attached to the side; the exterior
view displays the camouflaged
aspect of the shell as it is
normally found.

Superfamily **Carditacea**
Family **Carditidae**
Equivalve, inequilateral shells with two cardinal teeth
in one valve and one in the other. No pallial sinus.

Cardita bicolor
(Lamarck, 1822)

A beautiful shell, basically
creamy-white with brown spots
or markings, but sometimes
almost entirely brown. It has
strong flattened radiating ribs
which are weakly concentrically
striate, the interspaces being
narrow. Up to 55 mm. It is a
sand dweller, and we have found
it at Muscat, Sur, Salalah,
Masirah and the Khuriya
Muriya Islands. Distribution
general. Common.

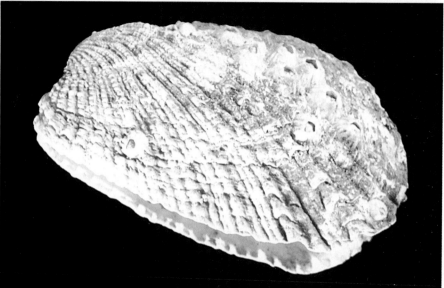

Cardita gubernaculum
Reeve, 1843

A thick shell with radial, scaly
somewhat irregular ribs. The
umbos are close to the anterior.
The exterior is brown, the
interior white tinged with
brown. Up to 45 mm. We have
found it in sand in shallow
water. Distribution Masirah
only. Rare.

Superfamily **Cardiacea**
Family **Cardiidae (Cockles)**

This is a well known family, many species being popular as food in many places in the world. Equivalve, inequilateral (usually) mostly ribbed shells.

There are two cardinal and two lateral teeth in each valve. Ligament external. No pallial sinus. The shells appear to be heart-shaped when the complete double shell is viewed from the side.

The animals prefer to live in sandy or muddy areas, often inhabiting the tidal estuaries, in shallow water. They have a large, sickle-shaped foot and short siphons.

Cardium pseudolima
Lamarck, 1819

This cockle is one of Oman's most beautiful molluscs. The colors vary from orange to yellow, pink and purple. It is a large, thick, heavy shell with flattened radial ribs. The living specimens are covered with fine hair-like bristles. Up to 150 mm. We have found it in mud flats, buried at the low-tide level with about one-fifth of the shell exposed. Distribution Masirah and the south coast of Oman. Locally common.

Cardium reeveanum
Dunker

This species has very prominent radial ornamentation, the ribs having "stepped" sides towards the anterior edge and there are wide interspaces between them. Up to 65 mm. We have found this species only at Salalah, where it lives just below the surface of the sand. Rare.

Laevicardium papyraceum
(Bruguière, 1789)

The shells of this species are thinner than those of most cockles and immature specimens show only a trace of the radial ribbing which becomes distinct in adults. There is often a purple blotch at the umbo. Up to 40 mm. We have found it in sand in shallow water. Distribution general. Very common.

Trachycardium lacunosum
(Reeve, 1845)

With strong radial ribs, close-set and having a "plaited" sculpture on them. The shells are somewhat elongated from umbo to anterior. The colors are pink, tan or purple blotches on a pale or white background. Up to 60 mm. We have found it in shallow water in sandy or muddy areas. Distribution general. Common.

Nemocardium aurantiacum
(Adams and Reeve, 1850)

This species has a distinctive sculptured exterior, with part of the shell smooth and part with noticeable diagonal sculpture. The color is primarily pink with red blotches towards the umbos. Up to 60 mm. We have found it in sand in shallow water, only at Masirah, Rare.

Superfamily **Tridacnacea**
Family **Tridacnidae (Giant Clams)**

Equivalve, inequilateral very heavy thick shells, fluted
and with an opening anterior to the umbos for the
byssus. Ligament external. Edges serrated and
interlocking. This family must not be confused with the
"Clams" which are used to make a particularly
delicious soup in the United States, which are in the
Veneridae. It is of interest to note that one species,
Tridacna gigas which is not found in Oman, can reach a
length of over four feet and weighs as much as 500 lbs.
It is the world's largest bivalve. The animal of
Tridacna is unusual in that it is a true "farmer"
cultivating algae on the inner side of its mantle. The
edible algae augment the animal's diet. In order to
grow algae, sunlight is necessary and hence Tridacna
will always be found in water shallow enough to allow
penetration of sunlight.

Tridacna maxima
(Roeding, 1798)

Typical members of the family,
fluted and frilled, living in
shallow water on coral reefs. Up
to 400 mm. Some of the shells
become very heavy weighing 30
or 40 pounds. People sometimes
use them as flower pots or door
stops. Distribution Masirah,
Salalah and at Sur, where dead
shells are very common.

Superfamily **Mactracea**
Family **Mactridae (Surf Clams)**
Equivalve, inequilateral shells, usually with two
cardinal and two lateral teeth in each valve. The
ligament is contained in an internal pit. There is a
pallial sinus.

Mactra glabrata lilacea
Lamarck, 1818

This is the commonest bivalve
on the Batinah coast beaches
where dead valves can be
collected by the thousand. The
shells are thin and shiny, with
shallow concentric striae. The
colors vary but blue, white, pink,
and purple tend to predominate.
The interior is often a shiny
purple. Up to 80 mm. The
animal lives in sand and we have
often found them in shallow
water. Distribution general.
Very uncommon. *Mactra olorina*
Phillipi and *Mactra fauroti*
Jousseaume are possibly
synonyms, but this family needs
considerable research and
revision.

Family **Mesodesmatidae**
Ligament mainly internal. Shell longer in the front of
the umbos than behind.

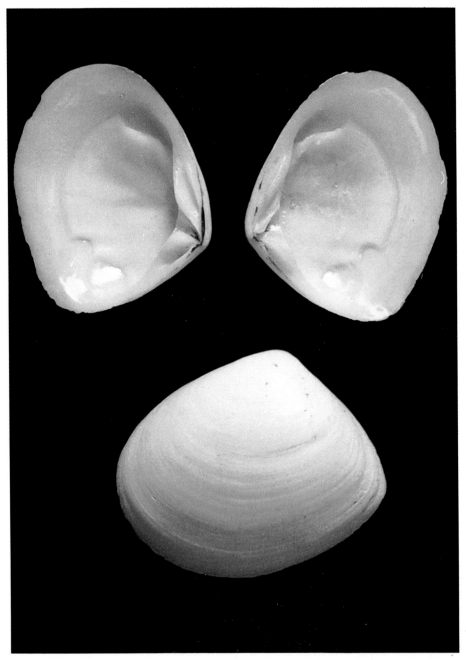

Mesodesma glabrata
(Gmelin, 1791)

A rather triangular shell,
rounded anteriorly and
posteriorly, with weak
concentric growth striae. The
pallial sinus is small. It has a thin
brown periostracum, often much
worn. Up to 40 mm. We have
found it in sand in shallow
water, only at Masirah. Rare.

Superfamily **Solenacea**
Family **Solenidae**
(Razor Shells or Jack-knife Clams)
Long, straight shells with parallel edges, truncated and
gaping at the ends. There is one cardinal tooth in each
valve. Ligament external.

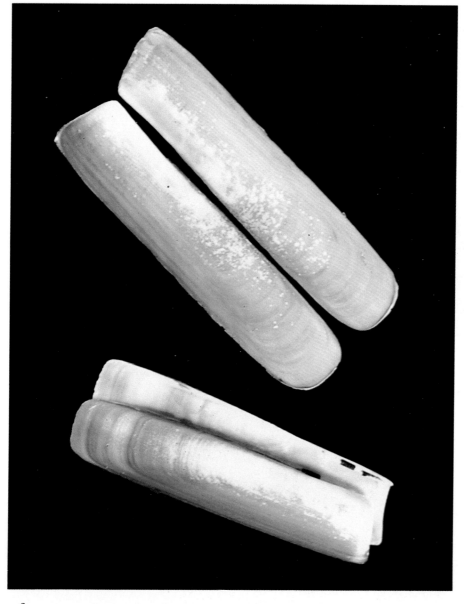

Solen brevis
Gray, 1832

Long shells, shaped like an old-
fashioned razor, with growth
lines parallel to the posterior and
dorsal edges and a thin brown
periostracum. The anterior edge
is curved. The ligament is short
and dark in color. Up to 95 mm.
These animals live in sand, in
which they can burrow with
astonishing speed attaining
depths of two or more feet in a
matter of seconds. Distribution
general. Very common.

Family **Cultellidae**
Similar to the Solenidae, but shorter and wider, with
the umbos not at the anterior, and with curved edges.

Siliqua japonica
(Dunker, 1861)

This shell is very thin and
fragile, with a strong internal rib
from the umbo to the dorsal edge
and a short ligament. It is so thin
that it is translucent. The colors
have a wide and unusual range,
from purple to light brown to
pink and yellowish, with three or
four broad white bands radiating
from the umbos and spreading
like light beams. Up to 80 mm.
Distribution general. Very
common.

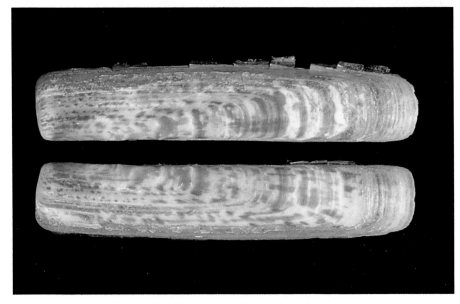

Phaxas cultellus
(Linnaeus, 1758)

Shell curved and narrower
at the anterior and posterior
ends than in the center. The
color is off-white speckled with
brown spots and lines. Up to
65 mm. Like the true razor-
shells this species can burrow
rapidly into the sand.
Distribution general. Rare.

Superfamily **Tellinacea**
Family **Tellinidae**
Equivalve, inequilateral shells, sometimes with a
twisted posterior end. Two double and one single
cardinal tooth in each valve. With or without lateral
teeth. External ligament. Deep pallial sinus.

Tellina rastellum
Hanley, 1844

These shells are sometimes
known as "sunrise shells"
because of the divergent rays of
pink which extend from the
umbos to the margin of the shell
in much the same way that
sunrays radiate into the sky at
sunrise. There are fine
concentric ridges, which are
scaly at the posterior and a
marked posterior keel and twist.
The shell is relatively thin but
not fragile. Up to 95 mm.
Distribution general.
Uncommon.

Tellina pharaonis
Hanley, 1844

An elongated shell with small
conspicuous umbos and
constricted posteriorly, with a
marked keel from the umbo to
the ventral edge and a twisted
posterior. Its elegant lines and
salmon pink color make it one of
Oman's most beautiful bivalves.
Up to 80 mm. The shell is
relatively thin and fragile and
dead specimens found on the
beaches are almost invariably
broken. Distribution general.
Uncommon.

Tellina foliacea
Linnaeus, 1758

This extremely handsome
species is bright orange in color
and has a glossy surface and a
serrated posterior edge. Up to 85
mm. It lives in sand in the low
intertidal zone and deeper
water. When the tide is way out
the shell can be found just below
the surface of the sand.
Distribution general but
particularly common on the
Batinah coast off As Sib and
Barka. Common.

Tellina wallaceae
Salisbury, 1934

This lovely, translucent white shell is very thin and fragile, and dead specimens are usually found broken. It is so thin that details of the anatomy of the animal within are visible in living specimens. Up to 45 mm. Distribution general. Uncommon.

Apolymetis angulata
(Gmelin, 1791)

A fragile, entirely white shell, with the pointed umbos near to the posterior which has a sharp keel in one valve matched by a furrow in the other. Up to 65 mm. We have found this species only at Muscat. Uncommon.

Tellina inflata
Gmelin, 1791

A white, fragile, almost triangular shell with a rounded anterior edge and a sharp posterior keel. There are fine growth lines. Up to 60 mm. Uncommon.

Apolymetis dubia
(Deshayes, 1854)

Similar in appearance to *Tellina inflata* but lacking the sharp posterior keel and not so inflated. Up to 40 mm. We have found this species only at Salalah. Uncommon.

Family **Donacidae (Wedge Shells)**
Equilateral, inequivalve, usually somewhat triangular flattish shells with two cardinal teeth in one valve and one in the other and sometimes two weak lateral teeth.

Donax scalpellum
Gray, 1857

Elongate shells with a short, angular posterior end and rounded anterior, slightly gaping at both ends. The exterior is glossy and smooth often decorated with several lavender radial bands. The interior is often pale purple. Up to 55 mm. We have found it in shallow water, just below the surface of the sand. In Salalah, we have often found it associated with seaweed. Distribution general. Common at Salalah but rare elsewhere.

Family **Psammobiidae (Garidae)**

Equivalve, inequilateral shells with one double and one single cardinal tooth in each valve. Ligament is external and prominent. There is often a brown periostracum. The shells of this family are mud and sand dwellers, often to be found in the intertidal zone where mud and sand mix. Most of the species have an attractive sculpture of concentric or radial striae and growth lines.

Gari maculosa
(Lamarck, 1818)

Sculptured by concentric striae, corrugated at the posterior end and crossed in the center of the shell by diagonal striae. The shell is relatively thin. The color varies considerably and the exterior is sometimes patterned with radiating rays. The living shells are covered with a brown periostracum. Up to 55 mm. We have found this species in muddy sand in the intertidal zone. Distribution general. Uncommon.

Asaphis deflorata
(Linnaeus, 1758)

Strong, heavy radially ridged shells which are often violet in color, though specimens which are paler or have colored rays can be found. Up to 70 mm. We have found this species in muddy sand or silt in the low intertidal zone. Distribution general. Uncommon.

Gari tripartita
(Deshayes, 1855)

The sculpture is distinctive: the anterior third of the shell has flattened concentric ridges, the center has sharper ridges, parallel to the edge of the shell and the posterior ridges are lamellose. The color ranges from pale pink to deep violet. Up to 65 mm. We have found this species in muddy sand in the intertidal zone. Distribution general. Uncommon.

Sanguinolaria cumingiana
(Deshayes, 1855)

Elongated oval shells, with small umbos and a small flat ligament shelf. The shell is thin and fragile, light blue, lavender or white in color and has a thin brown periostracum. Up to 75 mm. We have found this species usually in muddy sand. Distribution general. Common.

Family **Semelidae**

Equivalve, inequilateral shells with two to three cardinal teeth in each valve and usually lateral teeth as well. There is a deep rounded pallial sinus. The ligament is external and internal. The name "Semele" pronounced with three syllables, sem-e-lee, was originally the name of a colorful Greek goddess and this group of shells often display a wide range of colors, true to their namesake.

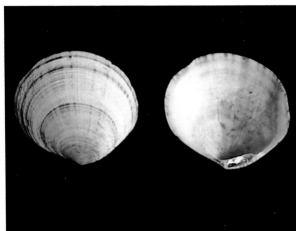

Semele sinensis
Reeve, 1850

A roundish, compressed, thin shell, with fine, concentric striae. The exterior is ivory, rayed with crimson to purple; the interior is glossy white, yellow flecked with red at the center. Up to 48 mm. Scientists who have observed the animal in salt water aquariums have reported that it can extend the siphons as much as six times the length of the shell. We have found this species only at Masirah. Rare.

Semele scabra
(Hanley, 1845)

This roundish, white bivalve is characterized by irregular concentric ridges which give it a crinkly appearance. The ridges are of different sizes in individual specimens. The surface has a dull, chalky appearance. Up to 58 mm. Distribution general. Uncommon.

Superfamily **Veneracea**
Family **Veneridae**
A large and variable family of bivalves, equivalve, mostly inequilateral, with three cardinal teeth (usually one double and one single) in each valve and lateral teeth present or absent. Pallial sinus sometimes deep and sometimes almost imperceptible. Lunule and escutcheon usually well developed, the lunule often heart-shaped, hence the name "Veneridae" after Venus, the goddess of love. Most species are sand-dwellers, but some live in rocks or among seaweed or coral.

Circenita callipyga
(Born, 1778)

This species is variable in sculpture, the concentric ribs being rugged and strong in some specimens and almost smooth in others. This variation has led to many synonyms and some authorities still consider some of the variants as distinct species. The color variations are also many, one variant with a strong zigzag pattern we have found only at Muscat. Up to 55 mm. The living mollusc can be found in the intertidal level in sand or mud or coarse gravel, the variation in habitat possibly causing the variation in shell sculpture. Distribution general. Very common.

Periglypta reticulata
(Linnaeus, 1758)

The shell has strong, concentric, notched lamellae which are serrated by distinct radial riblets. The color is cream with rusty markings. Up to 110 mm. Often the magnificent sculpture is hidden by encrustations which can be removed by soaking in bleach. We have usually found it in sand under rocks and frequently it has been found in association with *Conus achatinus* and *Conus pennaceus*, often living under the same rock within inches of each other. Distribution general. Fairly common.

Circe corrugata
(Dillwyn, 1817)

Characterized by the juvenile shell being sculptured with V-shaped ridges radiating from the umbos, the shell later becoming concentrically ridged. The lunule and escutcheon are marked with brown stripes. Up to 45 mm. Distribution general. Very common.

Gafrarium pectinatum
(Linnaeus, 1758)

Heavy, rounded, flattish shells with coarse nodulose concentric ribs and diverging ridges going diagonally towards the posterior edge for about one-third of the shell. Variably colored with patches or blotches of purple or brown on a paler background. Up to 30 mm. Distribution general. Found at Muscat, Salalah and Masirah. Rare.

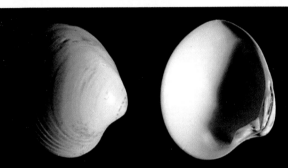

Amiantis umbonella
(Lamarck, 1818)

A heavy, shiny white shell with traces of brown. It is very inflated and the pallial sinus is sharply pointed. There is weak concentric ribbing on the exterior. Up to 55 mm. We have found it only at Muscat. Rare.

Circe intermedia
Reeve, 1864

Very similar to *Circe corrugata* and considered by some authorities to be a synonym. Rather more inflated, the concentric ridges rather stronger. Up to 60 mm. Distribution Masirah only. Rare.

Sunetta effossa
Hanley, 1843

The strong concentric ribs, dotted with subtle color changes from white to pink to reddish-brown, make this an unusually handsome species. The escutcheon is deeply indented, forming a flat shelf in the interior of the shell. Up to 55 mm. We have found it at low tide buried in the sand. Distribution probably general. Uncommon.

Callista erycina
(Linnaeus, 1758)

A very strong, solid attractive shell, the plaid patterned orange-brown markings making it very distinctive. There are weak to strong concentric ridges on the surface. The pallial sinus is moderately deep. Up to 95 mm. The animals can be found at low tide burrowing into the sand. Distribution general. Very common.

Tivela damaoides
(Gray, 1843)

A triangular, very heavy, strong shell, remarkable for its weight. Up to 120 mm, the shells from Masirah being larger than those from elsewhere. Distribution general. Very common.

Tivela mulawana
Biggs, 1969

Exteriorly this shell resembles a Donax, but the strong coarse hinge teeth distinguish it from that family. The coloring is extremely variable. Up to 42 mm. The type locality is Masirah. So far we have found it only at Masirah and at Salalah, where it is very common, dead.

Comus platyaulux
(Tomlin, 1924)

Distinguished by the broad flat concentric ribs which make this species very easily recognizable. The shell is inflated, the umbos have V-shaped ridges and the hinge teeth are coarse and strong. Color is brown, pink or red-brown on cream to ivory. Up to 50 mm. Distribution general. Uncommon.

Callista multiradiata
(Sowerby, 1851)

A paler colored version of
Callista erycina and not so
common.

Dosinia alta
(Dunker, 1848)

A rounded, glossy white shell,
with very fine, close, concentric
striations. The pallial sinus is
very deep and pointed. Up to 30
mm. To be found in sand at low
tide. Distribution general. Very
common.

Dosinia tumida
(Gray, 1838)

A heavy, glossy white shell with
fine concentric striations which
coarsen at the anterior and
posterior edges, becoming
almost prickly at the posterior.
The pallial sinus is moderately
deep and pointed. Up to 65 mm.
To be found just below the
surface of the sand. Distribution
general. Common.

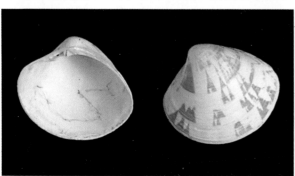

Lioconcha ornata
(Dillwyn, 1817)

A small, rounded shell, up to
20 mm, variously patterned
brown on bluish-ivory. There is
a deep pallial sinus. We have
found this only at Muscat. Rare.

Irus irus
(Linnaeus, 1758)

This species is often distorted due to its habit of nestling in crevices in rocks. The shell is dull and white and ornamented with rough white concentric lammellae. Up to 40 mm. Distribution general. Common, but difficult to find alive.

Marcia hiantina
(Lamarck, 1818)

A finely concentrically ridged shell, with a noticeable groove extending from the umbo to about one-third the way from the anterior end and a shallower groove towards the posterior. The exterior is cream in color, sometimes slightly patterned in brown. The interior is whitish to pinkish and the pallial sinus is moderately deep and rounded. Up to 55 mm. Distribution general. Common.

Tapes texturata
(Lamarck, 1818)

The surface is sculptured with shallow concentric lines and variously patterned with chevron-shaped markings of dark brown on cream. The interior is white, the pallial sinus shallow and pointed. Up to 38 mm. We have found this species only on the Batinah coast beaches. Uncommon.

Tapes bruguierei
(Hanley, 1845)

The exterior is finely concentrically striate and radially ridged, giving a cancellated appearance. The general pattern is of radiating rays of darker color on a paler background. The interior is glossy, cream to pink, with a deep rounded pallial sinus. The hinge teeth are fine. Up to 55 mm. We have found this species only on the Batinah coast beaches near Muscat. Uncommon.

Marcia species

Much more coarsely ridged than the other two species of Marcia to be found in Oman, the ridges at the posterior tending to divide or bifurcate. The exterior is grey cream to cream variously patterned with rays or zigzags of darker color. Up to 50 mm. Distribution general. Uncommon.

Paphia textile
(Gmelin, 1791)

An elongated, glossy, smooth shell, cream, decorated with chevron markings in dark brown, making this one of the handsomest of bivalves. The interior is white and the pallial sinus is shallow and squared-off at the end. Up to 80 mm. Distribution general. Common.

Marcia ceylonensis
(Lamarck, 1818)

A very smooth surfaced shell with a few weak concentric growth lines, similar in shape to *Marcia opima*. The exterior color is pale to deep cream, slightly patterned with brown or plain. The interior is white, the pallial sinus is rounded and deep. Up to 55 mm. It can be found in sand at low tide. Distribution general. Common.

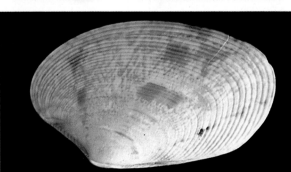

Paphia sulcaria
(Lamarck, 1818)

An elongated shell, resembling *Paphia textile* in shape, and in color pattern, but with strong, sharp coarse concentric ridges. The interior is white and the pallial sinus moderately deep and bluntly pointed. Up to 74 mm. Distribution general. Moderately common.

Paphia cf. textile variety

There is a plain brown species to be found in Oman which is possibly only a color variant of *Paphia textile*, but we have never found any specimens which intergrade. Up to 55 mm. Distribution general. Rare.

Bassina calophylla
(Philippi, 1836)

A striking white shell with prominent concentric upstanding ridges covering the entire surface. The edges of the ridges are slightly notched, thus giving the shell a lace-like appearance. Up to 35 mm. We have found this species only at Masirah. Rare.

Venerupis deshayesii
(Hanley, 1843)

A delicately patterned shell, the colors reminiscent of a moth's wing, purple-brown or brown on a lighter background, with fine concentric striations. A variety, found only at Muscat, has a deep purple band along the inner edge of the lip. Up to 75 mm. Distribution general, often found dead on the Batinah beaches. Common.

Paphia gallus
Gmelin, 1791

This is a sturdy species with a strong shell with many concentric coarse ridges. It is noticeable for the indentation in the edge of the shell at the posterior. The pale brown external color is interrupted by brown dots and dashes, thus presenting a striking appearance. Up to 65 mm. Distribution probably general: we have found it at Muscat, Sur, Salalah, Masirah and the Khuriya Muriya Islands. Uncommon.

Order **Myoida**

Superfamily **Myacea**
Family **Corbulidae (Basket Clams)**
Inequivalve, inequilateral small shells with a
ligamental pit in one valve, the left valve smaller than
the right, pallial sinus small or non-existent.

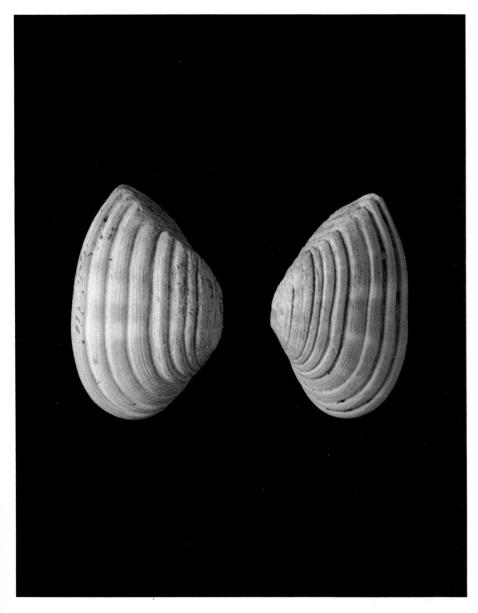

Corbula modesta
Hinds, 1843

An inflated shell with a marked
posterior keel, and coarse
concentric ridges, which in
themselves are finely
concentrically striate, the
interspaces being deep. White in
color. Up to 20 mm. This species
is a sand-dweller. Distribution is
probably general, though we
have found it only at Muscat.
Rare.

Family **Thracidae**
Inequilateral, slightly gaping shells, the left valve
usually smaller than the right. Spoon shaped process
inside the shell. Weak pallial sinus.

Thracia adenensis
Melvill, 1898

Delicate white shells, very
fragile. Up to 50 mm. We have
found this species living in sand
below the low tide level.
Sometimes after storms large
numbers of them are thrown up
on the Batinah coast beaches
and because the shell is so light it
is carried by wave action to the
highest point on the beach.
Distribution general. Common.

Cephalopoda

There are about 500 species in this Class. These are the squids, octupuses and nautiluses.

Class **Cephalopoda**
Subclass **Dibranchia**
Order **Octopoda**

Superfamily **Argonautidae (Paper Nautilus)**
This family is in the class Cephalopoda, which includes
the octopuses, squid or cuttlefish, and spirula. It is a
different family from that of the Chambered Nautilus,
Nautilus pompilius (Linnaeus), which has a true shell to
protect its soft body.

Marine molluscs without shells, internal or external.
The body and head are combined and the animal has
eight arms or tentacles. The animal swims by ejecting
water forcibly from a funnel. They are carnivorous.
The female argonaut has two arms especially adapted
to form and hold the "shell" which is in fact not a
molluscan shell in the true sense of the word, but a
cradle to hold and protect the eggs. The male is very
much smaller than the female, being only a few
centimeters long. They are mainly pelagic. When the
eggs are hatched the female releases the shell which
then gets cast up on the beaches.

Argonauta argo
(Linnaeus, 1758)

A thin, translucent, boat-shaped
shell, white with delicate
bifurcating ribs radiating from the
central coil, the tips of the ribs
touched with brown. Up to
200 mm. Distribution general.
Rare.

Argonauta hians
Solander, 1786

Similar in shape to *Argonauta argo* but with coarser ribs, ending in often open tubercules. The shell and the keel are wider and the aperture more flaring. The surface has a shagreened appearance. Up to 80 mm. Distribution general. Very common.

Glossary of terms

Abalone Common name for ear-shaped shells with nacreous interior; members of the Family Haliotidae.

Acuminate Pointed; tapering to a point.

Adduct To pull toward the center (median axis). Opposite of abduct.

Adductor muscle One or two muscles found in bivalve shells, which function by pulling the two valves together.

Algae A collective name given to a wide variety of plants ranging from microscopic plankton to sea weeds. Although the larger varieties remain in one locality, they do not have true roots.

Anterior The part of the shell nearest to the front of the mollusc when it moves. In gastropods, it is the head end of the animal, i.e. the opposite end to the shell's apex. In bivalves, where the foot emerges.

Aperture The principal opening in a shell, i.e. entrance to the shell's interior.

Apex The first part of a shell to be formed; usually pointed, and functioning as the summit of the gastropod spire.

Apical Pertaining to the apex or tip.

Arcuate Arched or curved.

Asymmetrical Unequal; where the structures on either side of a dividing line do not correspond exactly.

Axial In gastropod shells, in the direction or line of the axis, i.e. parallel to the axis of coiling.

Axis Imaginary line through the shell's apex extending centrally to the other end and around which are coiled the whorls of the gastropod shell.

Barnacle Not a mollusc. It is a Crustacean.

Base The last formed portion of the gastropod shell. Opposite end of the shell from the apex.

Beak The tip of the bivalve shell near the hinge. Also called the umbo.

Bifurcated Branched, double pronged; where lines originate close together and then diverge.

Biological community All living creatures in a given geographical area, and the inter-relationships between the various members.

Bivalves Molluscs with two separate parts (valves) connected by a hinge.

Body whorl The last formed whorl of a spiral shell.

Byssus Thread-like fibrous strands secreted by bivalves for the purpose of attachment to solid objects.

Calcareous Composed of, or, containing significant amounts of calcium carbonate.

Callus A deposit of shelly material.

Cancellate Interlacing threads or lines creating a lattice-work.

Carnivorous Creatures that live by eating animal tissues, as opposed to creatures that eat plants.

Caudal Pertaining to the tail or rear portion of the body.

Chlorophyll The chemical substance which enables green plants to utilize the energy in sunlight in making high-energy nutrients. The green coloring matter in plants.

Cilia Hair-like filaments which are outgrowths of certain cells and are capable of vibrating or rhythmic motion.

Columella The pillar surrounding the axis of a gastropod shell. The opposite side of the aperture from the lip.

Concentric Ridges or striae which coincide in direction with the growth lines of bivalve shells.

Corneous Horn-like in consistency.

Crenulated Having a regularly notched edge.

Ctenidia The respiratory organs of molluscs, consisting of a series of comb-like structures. In bivalves, the ctenidia are modified for feeding purposes.

Decussate Having oblique intersecting lines or ribs creating a latticed configuration.

Dentate Having teeth or tooth-like protuberances.

Deposit feeders Molluscs that feed on material which has settled on the ocean floor.

Depressed Low in proportion to the diameter.

Dextral "Right-handed." Term applied to gastropod shell which has the aperture on the observer's right when the apex of the shell is held upwards. Opposite of sinistral.

Dorsum The back of the shell, opposite to the aperture in gastropods.

Edentulous Lacking teeth.

Endemic Restricted to a specific geographical area.

Equivalvular Having two valves of equal size and shape.

Erythraean Region The Red Sea and adjacent areas.

Filiform Thread-like, fine and slender.

Filter-feeders Molluscs which feed by filtering food particles from the sea water passing through the gills (Ctenidia).

Fimbriated Fringed.

Fissure A narrow cleft.

Fusiform Spindle-shaped, elongate.

Gape Space between the valves of a bivalve shell when it is closed.

Gaping Not closed tightly.

Gill The breathing organ of molluscs.

Globose Ball-shaped. Rounded. Spherical.

Granulated Covered with small tubercules or granules. Pustular.

Growth-lines One or more lines on the surface of a shell indicating former growth margins. (Growth periods alternate with rest periods).

Herbivorous Feeding on plant matter rather than animal matter.

Hermit crab A soft-bellied crustacean with claws which occupies univalve shells.

Hinge The interlinking and often toothed structure in a bivalve mollusc where the two parts remain in continuous contact.

Hinge plate The portion of the hinge bearing the teeth and sockets.

Holotype The single specimen designated by the author in describing the species, and serving as the "type" of that species.

Hybrid The offspring produced by interbreeding of two different biological species. A hybrid is not fertile and therefore is unable to reproduce.

Imbricated Overlapped, as with tiles on a roof.

Inequivalvular Having one valve larger than the other.

Inflated Ventricose, swollen, puffed-up.

Keel A ridge.

Labial teeth Tooth-like processes at the inner edge of the aperture of some gastropods, especially the cowries, which look like, but do not function as, teeth.

Lamellated Covered with scales or thin plates.

Ligament The elastic, corneous, structure joining the two parts of bivalve shells.

Lip The margin of the aperture.

Lirate Sculptured with fine thread-like ridges.

Maculated Spotted or dotted.

Mantle The fleshy, curtain-like outer layer of the molluscan body which secretes the shell. In some species, it forms tubular folds which make up the inhalant and exhalant siphons.

Margin The edge or border of a shell.

Nacreous Consisting of thin leaves of aragonite lying parallel to the inner surface of the shell creating a lustrous appearance like mother-of-pearl.

Neustons Organisms which live at the air-water interface, among, but not members of, the plankton.

Nodose Nodular. Having tubercules or knobs.

Operculum Calcareous or horny structure attached to the foot of many molluscs, which when retracted, serves to close or partly close the aperture of the shell.

Ornament Surface sculpture or pattern which stands out in relief on the exterior of a shell.

Ovate Egg-shaped.

Pallial line An impression on the interior of both sides of the bivalve shell, indicating the attachment of the mantle.

Paratype A specimen from the same lot as the Holotype, used by the author in the original description of the species, but not the "type" of the species.

Pelagic Related to the ocean surface.

Periostracum The outer fibrous or corneous layer made up of conchiolin, which covers the shell of many molluscs.

Phytoplankton The plant members of the plankton community.

Plankton Tiny organisms, mostly microscopic, which drift passively in the ocean, and which form the basic oceanic food.

Plicate Folded or plaited.

Pre-occupied A name invalidated because a previous author used the same term or combination of terms for a different kind of animal.

Protoconch The embryonal portion (apical whorls) of the gastropod shell which often differs in size and sculpture from later whorls.

Punctate Minute depressions like pin-pricks.

Pustule Small protuberance or tubercule.

Pyriform Pear-shaped.

Quadrate Square or rectangular in general outline.

Radial Directed from the umbo (beak) toward the margins. Spreading rays as sunbeams.

Radula Serial rows of flexible teeth (toothed ribbon) which serve as a rasping or drilling organ for gastropods.

Reticulate Similar to cancellate. Lattice-like sculpturing caused by threads or ridges of ornament.

Rib A prominent elevation on the shell's surface, usually occurring as a continuous line.

Salinity The relative salt content.

Scabrous Roughened and irregular.

Sessile Remaining in one place. Not moving.

Sinistral "Left-handed". Term applied to gastropod shell which has the aperture on the observer's left when the apex of the shell is held upwards. Opposite of dextral.

Siphon Tube-like fold of the mantle used for passage of water, whether inhalant or exhalant.

Spinose Having thorn-like protuberances or spines.

Stria Incised fine groove on the shell's surface.

Striation Grooved sculpturing.

Stromboid notch A cleft in the apertural margin characteristic of shells in the family Strombidae.

Substrate The part beneath. Foundation. The sea floor on which, or in which, a mollusc lives.

Suspension feeders Molluscs that eat material which is suspended in the ocean water.

Suture The continuous spiral line on the gastropod shell where the whorls join.

Synonym Two or more names for one species.

Teeth Term loosely applied to structures on the outer lip of gastropod shells, particularly the cowries. The name is given because of the resemblance to mammalian teeth, but the cowrie's "teeth" do not serve a masticating function.

Trochophore A free-swimming ciliated larva of certain aquatic invertebrates.

Truncate Sharply or abruptly cut off.

Tubercule Elevated, knob-like protrusion. Pustule.

Tumid Swollen.

Turbinate Turban-shaped, broadly conical.

Turreted Tower-shaped with a long spire. Stepped.

Umbilicus Navel-like. A depressed cavity or hole around which the inner surface of the gastropod shell is coiled. The open axis of coiling.

Umbo Beak. Earliest formed portion of the bivalve shell.

Univalve A mollusc consisting of a single shell.

Univalvular Having only one valve, as opposed to bivalves which have two valves.

Up-welling An ocean phenomenon where deep water moves upward to the surface.

Varicose Abnormally and irregularly swollen or dilated. Thickened.

Varix Thickening at an axial growth stage, which marks a former outer lip margin.

Veliger Molluscan larva in the free-swimming stage.

Ventral Toward the belly. The inner or lower surface. In bivalves, the region of the shell opposite to the hinge. In univalves, the apertural side of the shell. Opposite to dorsal.

Ventricose Swollen. Inflated.

Whorl One complete turn (360°) of a coiled gastropod shell around its imaginary axis.

Wing A more or less elongated terminal portion of a shell usually of the families Pectinacea or Pteriacea.

Zooplankton The animal members of the plankton community.

Bibliography

General Reference Books, Scientific Journals, and Articles pertaining to our area.

Abbott, R. Tucker *Indo-Pacific Mollusca*. Vols: I to III. Philadelphia.
Abbott, R. Tucker *Monographs of Marine Mollusca*. Vol: I. Greenville.
Abbott, R. Tucker 1973. *Acteon eloiseae*, a new opisthobranch from Arabia. *Nautilus, 87*: 91–92
Abbott, R. Tucker 1972. *Kingdom of the Seashell*. New York. (Routledge)
Abbott, R. Tucker and Lewis, H. 1970. *Cymatium boschi*, new species from the Arabian Sea. *Nautilus, 83*: 86–88.
Allan, Joyce 1956. *Cowry Shells of the World*. Sydney. (Georgian House)

Basson, P. W., Burchard, J. E., Hardy, J. T., & Price, A. 1977. *Biotopes of the Western Arabian Gulf*. Dhahran, Saudi Arabia.
Biggs, H. E. J. 1969. Marine Mollusca of Masirah I., South Arabia. *Arch. Moll. 99*: 201–207.
Burgess, C. M. 1970. *The Living Cowries*. New York. (Barnes)

Cameron, R. 1961. *Shells*. London. (Putnams)
Carson, Rachel 1955. *Under the Sea Wind*. New York. (Oxford University Press)
Cate, C. N. 1964. Western Australian Cowries. *Veliger, 7*: 212–232.
Cernohorsky, W. O. 1972. *Marine Shells of the Pacific Volume II*. Sydney. (Pacific Publications)
Cernohorsky, W. O. 1978. *Tropical Pacific Marine Shells*. Sydney. (Pacific Publications)
Clayton, J. M. 1974. *Seashells*. London. (Octopus Books)
Clover, P. W. 1968. *A Catalog of Popular Marginella Species*. New York.
Clover, P. W. 1972. Description of a new species of *Conus* from South East Arabia. *Venus, 31*: 117.
Clover, P. W. 1974. Three new species of Marginellidae from the Indian Ocean. *Journal of Conchology*, London, *28*: 213–216.

Dance, S. P. 1966. *Shell Collecting. An Illustrated History*. London. (Faber and Faber)
Dance, S. P. 1969. *Rare Shells*. London. (Faber and Faber)
Dance, S. P. 1971. *Seashells*. London. (Hamlyn)
Dance, S. P. 1974. *The Encyclopedia of Shells*. Poole. (Blandford)

Deas, W. 1974. *Seashells of Australia*. Sydney. (Rigby)

Engel, L. 1961. *The Sea*. New York. (Time Incorporated, Ltd)

Hage, Tadashige 1971. Shells of the Pacific. Osaka. (Hoikusha Publishing Co.)
Hawaian Shell News, The. Published by the Hawaian Malacological Society, Honolulu.
Hinton, A. G. 1972. *Shells of New Guinea and the Central Indo-Pacific*. Port Moresby. (Jacaranda Press)
Hornell, J. 1951. *Indian Molluscs*. Bombay Natural History Society.

Kilburn, R. N. 1977. A Revision of the Naticidae of Southern Africa and Mozambique. *Annals of Natal Museum, 2*: 829–884.
Kira, Tetsuaki 1962. *Shells of the Western Pacific in Color*. Osaka. (Hoikusha Publishing Co)
Kohn, A. J. 1978. The Conidae (Mollusca: Gastropoda) of India. *Journal of Natural History, 12*: 295–335.

Lindner, G. 1977. *Seashells of the World*. Poole. (Blandford)

Maclean, J. H. 1971. A revised classification of the family Turridae, with the proposal of new subfamilies, genera and subgenera from the Eastern Pacific. *Veliger, 14*: 114–130.
Marsh, J. A. and Rippingale, O. H. 1964. *Cone Shells of the World*. Melbourne. (Jacaranda Press)
Melvin, A. G. 1967. *Sea Shells of the World*. Rutland, Vermont. (Charles E. Tuttle Co)
Moore, R. C. 1960. *Treatise on Invertebrate Paleontology Part I Mollusca 1*. Lawrence, Kansas.
Moore, R. C. 1969. *Treatise on Invertebrate Paleontology Part N Mollusca 6*. 3 vols. Lawrence, Kansas.
Morton, J. E. 1960. *Mollusks*. New York. (Harper & Brothers)

Oliver, A. P. H. 1975. *Shells of the World*. London. (Hamlyn)

Platt, R. 1949. Shells Take You Over World Horizons. *National Geographic Magazine, 96*: 33–84.

Radwin, G. E. & D'Attilio, A. 1976. *Murex Shells of the World*. Stanford University Press

Rogers, J.E. 1951. *The Shell Book*. Boston. (Chas. T. Blandford)

Saul, M. 1974. *Shells*. London. (Hamlyn)
Smythe, K.R. 1972. Marine Mollusca from Bahrain Island. *Journal of Conchology, 27*: 491–496.
Smythe, K.R. 1979. The Marine Mollusca of the United Arab Emirates, Arabian Gulf. *Journal of Conchology, 30*: 57–80.
Solem, A. 1974. *The Shell Makers*. New York. (John Wiley & Sons)
Stix, H. & M. and Abbott, R.T. *The Shell. Five Hundred Million Years of Inspired Design*. New York. (Harry N. Abrams)

Taylor, D.W. & Sohl, N.F. 1962. An outline of Gastropod Classification. *Malacologia, 1*: 7–32.
Taylor, J. & Walls, J.G. 1975. *Cowries*. Neptune City, New Jersey. (T.F.H. Publications).
Townsend, F.W. 1928. Notes on Shell Collecting in the Northern parts of the Arabian Sea, including the Gulfs of Oman and Persian Gulf in the years 1890–1914. *Proceedings of the Malacological Society, London, 18*: 118–126.

Veliger, The. Published by the Californian Malacozoological Society.

Wagner, R.J.L. & Abbott, R.T. 1978. *Standard Catalog of Shells*. Greenville. (American Malacologists Inc.)
Wagner, R.J.L. & Abbott, R.T. 1964. *Van Nostrand's Standard Catalog of Shells*. New York.
Walls, J.G. 1979. *Cone Shells*. Neptune City, N.J. (T.F.H.) Publications incorp.) 1019 pp. illustrated.
Webb, W.F. Fifth Edition, undated. *Recent Mollusca*. Wellesley Hills, Mass.
Wenz, W. & Zilch, A. 1938–1961. *Handbuch der Paläozoologie*, I & II, Berlin.
Wilson, B.R. & Gillett, K. 1971. *Australian Shells*. Sydney. (A.H. & A.W. Reed)

Yonge, C.M. & Thompson, T.E. 1976. *Living Marine Molluscs*. London. (Collins)

Index